Evening Standard

GIANT

Book of over 200 Quick Crosswords No. 5

**YOUR FAVOURITE QUICK
PUZZLES RE-PRINTED
FROM THE EVENING
STANDARD**

Answers are at the back of the book

**Published by
Harmsworth Magazines Limited
on behalf of the Evening Standard
London W8 5TT**

ISBN 085144 658 2

Distributed by: Comag, Tavistock Road,
West Drayton, Middlesex UB7 7QE
(Newstrade) and Biblios, Partridge Green,
Sussex RH13 8LD (book trade).

Typeset by Datix International Limited, Bungay, Suffolk
Printed in Australia by McPherson's Printing Group

1

ACROSS

4 Robust (5)
7 Peruser (6)
9 Crowd (3)
10 Summit (3)
12 Lariat (5)
13 Mass (4)
15 Beleaguer (5)

DOWN

1 Frisk (6)
2 Non-professional (6)
3 Fixed (3)
4 Cavity (4)
5 Diminish (5)
6 Anguish (8)

17 Detain (6)
19 Nobleman (4)
20 Boat (5)
22 Brown (3)
24 Bet (7)
27 Equality (3)
28 Delete (5)
31 Primadonna (4)

8 Gown (4)
11 Plaguing (9)
14 Bow (4)
16 Asterisk (4)
18 Harvest (4)
21 Height (8)
23 Want (4)
25 Entrance (4)
26 Sketched (4)

33 Firewood (6)
35 View (5)
37 Envelop (4)
38 Share (5)
39 Breach (3)
41 Moose (3)
42 Athlete (6)
43 Gem (5)

29 Rank (6)
30 Die (6)
32 Flower (5)
34 Close (4)
36 Shout (4)
40 Whelp (3)

2

ACROSS

1 Dawdle (6)
5 Rammed (6)
9 Broaden (5)
10 Laboured (6)
11 Donating (6)
12 Send (5)
14 Roguish (4)

17 Managed (3)
18 Fever (4)
20 True (5)
22 Demon (5)
23 Ordained (7)
24 Worried (5)
26 Material (5)
29 Responsibility (4)

30 Males (3)
32 Dandy (4)
33 Glory 5)
35 Clothes (6)
36 Fall (6)
37 Bar (5)
38 Rise (6)
39 Pay (6)

DOWN

1 Deadly (6)
2 Foolishness (6)
3 Pitcher (4)
4 Jockey (5)
5 Start (5)
6 One (4)
7 Pang (6)

8 Stubborn (6)
13 Wed (7)
15 Tree (5)
16 Hell (5)
18 Helped (5)
19 Unfastened (5)
21 Guided (3)
22 Dined (3)
24 Cigar (6)

25 Rural (6)
27 Figure (6)
28 Simply (6)
30 Quietened (5)
31 Famous (5)
33 Oven (4)
34 Certain (4)

Evening Standard

3

ACROSS

3 Polish (5)
9 Beverage (6)
10 Engraved (6)
11 Agree (5)
12 Ogle (4)
15 Dread (4)
17 Furious (7)

20 Fasten (3)
21 Automaton (5)
23 Eager (4)
25 Terrible (4)
26 Old-fashioned (5)
28 Expert (3)
30 Fall (7)
33 Thaw (4)

35 Toy (4)
36 Under (5)
38 Region (6)
39 Beat (6)
40 Cap (5)

DOWN

1 Climb (5)
2 Tender (5)
3 Obtain (3)
4 Guide (6)
5 Vend (4)
6 Pig-pen (3)
7 Pane (5)

8 Worship (5)
13 Heighten (7)
14 Swift (5)
16 Illness (7)
18 Slept (5)
19 Record (3)
22 Ruse (5)
24 Age (3)
27 Decipher (6)

28 Entertain (5)
29 Choose (5)
31 Sea-duck (5)
32 God (5)
34 Lake (4)
36 Crop (3)
37 Damp (3)

4

ACROSS

1 Victim (6)
5 Moist (4)
8 Slumber (5)
9 Tavern (3)
10 Excuse (4)
11 Achievement (4)

12 Longed (5)
13 Merited (6)
16 Dreadful (4)
18 Voucher (4)
20 Vehicle (3)
22 Boy (3)
23 Consume (3)
24 Auction (4)
25 Pour (4)

28 Disperse (6)
30 Kind (5)
32 Tolerate (4)
33 Curve (4)
34 Entrap (3)
35 Flat (5)
36 Watched (4)
37 Repaired (6)

DOWN

1 Tremble (6)
2 Unusual (8)
3 Torn (6)
4 Eased (9)
5 Guard (7)
6 Imitated (4)
7 Compassion (4)

8 Ocean (3)
14 Troubled (9)
15 Mine (3)
17 Fish-eggs (3)
19 Occurred (8)
20 Tin (3)
21 Venerated (7)
26 Centre (6)
27 Exhilarated (6)

29 Competent (4)
30 Violent wind (4)
31 Fish (3)

Evening Standard ═══

5

ACROSS

1 Zest (5)
5 Straight (6)
8 Goodbye (5)
10 Oozed (6)
11 Masculine (4)
14 Promise (6)
15 Widespread (7)

18 Finish (3)
19 Youth (3)
21 Sort (4)
23 Change (5)
24 Slipped (4)
27 Longing (3)
29 Performed (3)
31 Ludicrous (7)
32 Bird (6)

34 Ancestry (4)
35 Whole (6)
38 Cancel (5)
39 Tattered (6)
40 Docking-place (5)

DOWN

2 Employ (3)
3 Knocked (6)
4 Poem (3)
5 Rubbish-tip (4)
6 Soften (6)
7 Steal (6)
9 Perfectly (7)

12 Beer (3)
13 Whirlpool (4)
16 Wicked (4)
17 Subsequently (5)
20 Inhabitant (7)
22 Election (4)
24 Meal (6)
25 Image (4)

26 Plunging (6)
28 Small (6)
30 Lair (3)
33 Peruse (4)
36 Gist (3)
37 Groove (3)

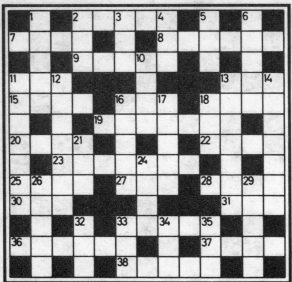

6

ACROSS

2 Irrigate (5)
7 Footwear item (4)
8 Slumbering (6)
9 Linger (5)
11 Serpent (3)
13 Colour (3)

15 Girdle (4)
16 Chart (3)
18 Auction (4)
19 Erased (7)
20 Lengthy (4)
22 Cultivate (4)
23 Revolving (7)
25 Observed (4)
27 Plaything (3)

28 Divide (4)
30 Concealed (3)
31 Untruth (3)
33 Managed (5)
36 Ebb (6)
37 Impel (4)
38 Old-fashioned (5)

DOWN

1 Picked (5)
2 Damp (3)
3 Hill (3)
4 Beam (3)
5 Aged (3)
6 Spree (5)
10 Genuine (4)

11 End (7)
12 Put in the ground (7)
13 Fundamental (7)
14 Puncture (7)
16 Intended (5)
17 Coin (5)
18 Fixed (3)

21 Firearm (3)
24 Jot (4)
26 Sea-duck (5)
29 Crest (5)
32 Males (3)
33 Dined (3)
34 Groove (3)
35 Defective (3)

Evening Standard

7

ACROSS

2 Stop (5)
7 Memorise (5)
8 Beneath (5)
10 Worship (5)
12 Rodent (3)
13 Oven (5)
15 Lured (7)

DOWN

1 Cogs (5)
2 Desire (5)
3 Charm (6)
4 Tender (4)
5 Scorned (7)
6 Inn (5)
9 Resin (3)

17 Twine (6)
19 Wand (3)
20 Recounted (7)
23 Finished (4)
25 Notch (4)
26 Responded (7)
30 Ocean (3)
31 Death (6)
34 Make ready (7)

11 Furious (7)
13 Endured (5)
14 Command (5)
16 Child (3)
18 State (7)
21 Liability (5)
22 Guide (5)
24 Revere (7)
27 Vegetable (3)

37 Elector (5)
38 Mineral (3)
39 Mistake (5)
40 Lax (5)
41 Accepted (5)
42 Flat (5)

28 Dedicate (6)
29 Amusing (5)
32 Virtuous (5)
33 Drain (5)
35 Epoch (3)
36 Gaelic (4)

8

ACROSS

1 Grasp (4)
4 Whim (3)
6 Candid (4)
8 Clergyman (6)
9 Bestow (6)
10 Moose (3)
12 Stadium (5)

14 Tendency (5)
15 Run off (5)
18 Glared (6)
20 Waist-belt (6)
24 Doctrine (5)
26 Hinge (5)
28 Factory (5)
30 Guided (3)
32 God-like (6)

33 Bird-house (6)
34 Standard (4)
35 Enthusiast (3)
36 Sketched (4)

DOWN

2 Monarch (5)
3 Spouse (7)
4 Front (4)
5 Harbour (4)
6 Proprietor (5)
7 Everlasting (7)
11 Circuit (3)

12 Donkey (3)
13 Beer (3)
16 Queer (3)
17 Ovum (3)
19 Petty (7)
21 Devil (3)
22 Revived (7)
23 Newt (3)
25 Poem (3)

27 Due (5)
29 Courage (5)
30 Petal (4)
31 Daybreak (4)

Evening Standard

9

ACROSS

1 Entitled (6)
5 Gap (6)
8 Elegant (8)
9 Unusual (4)
10 Through (3)
12 Tumbler (5)
15 Drunkard (3)
17 Stray (3)
18 Faucet (3)
19 Objective (3)
20 Elude (5)
21 Vase (3)
22 Wrath (3)
23 Tune (3)
24 Fruit (3)
26 Vision (5)
29 And not (3)
33 Store (4)
34 Contemplate (8)
35 Actor (6)
36 Shouted (6)

DOWN

2 Concur (5)
3 Fortune (4)
4 Dribble (5)
5 Foundation (5)
6 Nobleman (4)
7 Freight (5)
10 Unadorned (5)
11 Send (5)
12 Avarice (5)
13 Astonish (5)
14 Vapour (5)
15 Reject (5)
16 Singer (5)
25 Normal (5)
27 Happen again (5)
28 Irritate (5)
30 Fat (5)
31 Whirlpool (4)
32 Account (4)

10

ACROSS

1 Cease (4)
4 Beaker (3)
6 Expense (4)
9 Bird (3)
10 Acclaim (8)
11 One (4)
14 Tear (3)
16 Scrap (5)
19 Carping (8)
21 Dullard (5)
23 Scribbled (8)
24 Postpone (5)
27 Headgear (3)
31 Vessel (4)
33 Journalist (8)
34 Expire (3)
35 Clutched (4)
36 Deity (3)
37 Venture (4)

DOWN

2 Sort (4)
3 Pallid (4)
4 Careful (8)
5 Nobleman (4)
6 Divan (5)
7 Possess (3)
8 Slip (5)
12 Pungent (5)
13 Horrify (5)
14 Free (3)
15 Strike (5)
17 Respond (5)
18 Shabby (5)
20 Discarded (8)
22 Consume (3)
25 Wear away (5)
26 Performed (5)
28 Boast (4)
29 Trampled (4)
30 Prophet (4)
32 Sicken (3)

Evening Standard

11

ACROSS

4 Art (5)
7 Recover (6)
9 Firearm (3)
10 For each (3)
12 Circular (5)
13 Challenge (4)
15 Renovate (5)

17 Come (6)
19 Intellect (4)
20 Forbidden (5)
22 Consume (3)
24 Austere (7)
27 Stretch (3)
28 Skinflint (5)
31 Lengthy (4)
33 Bug (6)

35 Jousting-
weapon (5)
37 Direction (4)
38 Exclude (5)
39 Spike (3)
41 Performed (3)
42 Gift (6)
43 Stuck (5)

DOWN

1 Kudos (6)
2 Beetle (6)
3 Beaker (3)
4 Certain (4)
5 Recognised (5)
6 Tongue (8)
8 Fairy (4)

11 Veneration (9)
14 Cupid (4)
16 Tidy (4)
18 Cord (4)
21 Tree-dwelling
(8)
23 Domesticated
(4)
25 Related (4)

26 Pleasant (4)
29 Said (6)
30 Revolve (6)
32 Clearing (5)
34 Chair (4)
36 Parched (4)
40 Beam (3)

12

ACROSS

1 Whole (6)
5 Grasp (6)
9 Entertainment (5)
10 Excuse (6)
11 Sterile (6)
12 Females (5)
14 Guide (4)
17 Free (3)
18 Joke (4)
20 Consumer (5)
22 Assesses (5)
23 Ripened (7)
24 Storehouse (5)
26 Rot (5)
29 Paradise (4)
30 Network (3)
32 Valley (4)
33 Hell (5)
35 Hammer (6)
36 Metal (6)
37 Respond (5)
38 Totter (6)
39 Warmed (6)

DOWN

1 Transfix (6)
2 Menace (6)
3 Exult (4)
4 Singer (5)
5 Diced (5)
6 Thin (4)
7 Gullet (6)
8 Passed (6)
13 Mistreated (7)
15 Relaxed (5)
16 Fiend (5)
18 Exhausted (5)
19 Foot-lever (5)
21 Rodent (3)
22 Colour (3)
24 Considered (6)
25 Stripped (6)
27 Chest (6)
28 Shouted (6)
30 Irrigate (5)
31 Seat (5)
33 Present (4)
34 Location (4)

Evening Standard

13

ACROSS

3 Confess (5)
9 Fleet (6)
10 Tremble (6)
11 Sag (5)
12 Inactive (4)
15 Shortage (4)
17 Effective (7)

20 Enemy (3)
21 Rasp (5)
23 Irritation (4)
25 Nobleman (4)
26 Symbol (5)
28 Favourite (3)
30 Propriety (7)
33 Thought (4)
35 Speed (4)

36 Surpass (5)
38 Uncertain (6)
39 Charm (6)
40 Knife-edge (5)

DOWN

1 Custom (5)
2 Little (5)
3 Append (3)
4 Audacious (6)
5 Image (4)
6 Gratuity (3)
7 Bundle (5)

8 Shattered (5)
13 Invented (7)
14 Choose (5)
16 Gather (7)
18 Avarice (5)
19 Consumed (3)
22 Keen (5)
24 Heated (3)
27 Required (6)

28 Annoyance (5)
29 Torment (5)
31 Called (5)
32 Long (5)
34 Fight (4)
36 Sphere (3)
37 Unit (3)

14

ACROSS

1 Oppose (6)
5 Box (4)
8 Lid (5)
9 Animal (3)
10 Space (4)
11 Vacant (4)
12 Rate (5)
13 Sturdy (6)
16 Secure (4)
18 Cheese (4)
20 Married (3)
22 Entrap (3)
23 Lair (3)
24 Broad (4)
25 Pour (4)
28 Dedicate (6)
30 Traded (5)
32 Foundation (4)
33 Jot (4)
34 Spoil (3)
35 Untidy (5)
36 Reared (4)
37 Offer (6)

DOWN

1 Observe (6)
2 Tripped (8)
3 Emphasise (6)
4 Finished (9)
5 Cut (7)
6 Poke (4)
7 Discourteous (4)
8 Lettuce (3)
14 Torment (9)
15 Male (3)
17 Charge (3)
19 Disfigured (8)
20 Intelligence (3)
21 Erased (7)
26 Threat (6)
27 Dread (6)
29 Snatch (4)
30 Cupola (4)
31 Plaything (3)

Evening Standard ====

15

ACROSS

1 Beg (5)
5 Seem (6)
8 Municipal (5)
10 Sausage (6)
11 Damage (4)
14 Flag (6)
15 Shortage (7)

18 Weight (3)
19 Faucet (3)
21 Require (4)
23 Beverage (5)
24 Fashionable (4)
27 Tear (3)
29 Steal from (3)
31 Teaching (7)

32 Deceived (6)
34 Observe (4)
35 Sudden (6)
38 Strayed (5)
39 Yelled (6)
40 Moribund (5)

DOWN

2 Meadow (3)
3 Shrub (6)
4 Obscure (3)
5 Pain (4)
6 Clergyman (6)
7 Spoilt (6)
9 Caller (7)

12 Insect (3)
13 Pit (4)
16 Every (4)
17 Implicit (5)
20 Well-liked (7)
22 Therefore (4)
24 Chest (6)
25 Press (4)
26 Hue (6)

28 Robust (6)
30 Wager (3)
33 Act (4)
36 Cot (3)
37 Enclosure (3)

16

ACROSS

2 Kindle (5)
7 Loyal (4)
8 Decorated (6)
9 Suspect (5)
11 Beret (3)
13 Tooth (3)

15 Responsibility (4)
16 Fix (3)
18 Pallid (4)
19 Barricade (7)
20 Season (4)
22 Mail (4)
23 Moment (7)
25 Remit (4)

27 Newt (3)
28 Island (4)
30 Label (3)
31 Fish (3)
33 Van (5)
36 Figurine (6)
37 Above (4)
38 Dissuade (5)

DOWN

1 Harmonium (5)
2 Guided (3)
3 Animal (3)
4 Child (3)
5 Tavern (3)
6 Seat (5)

10 Ale (4)
11 Competition (7)
12 Sweet (7)
13 Revel (7)
14 Refined (7)
16 Adhesive (5)
17 Allow (5)
18 Vitality (3)

21 Finish (3)
24 Abroad (4)
26 Soil (5)
29 Flat (5)
32 Consumed (3)
33 Nourished (3)
34 Unconscious (3)
35 Hill (3)

Evening Standard

17

ACROSS

2 Flashy (5)
7 Youngster (5)
8 Proprietor (5)
10 Leading (5)
12 Tune (3)
13 Commerce (5)
15 Polluted (7)
17 Venerate (6)
19 Healthy (3)
20 Penetrated (7)
23 Agitate (4)
25 Clergyman (4)
26 Extinct (7)
30 Vehicle (3)
31 Festival (6)
34 Formal (7)
37 Mode (5)
38 Bird (3)
39 Same (5)
40 Slip (5)
41 Strayed (5)
42 Screen (5)

DOWN

1 Portion (5)
2 Clearing (5)
3 Stick (6)
4 Deceased (4)
5 Expected (7)
6 Cap (5)
9 Nothing (3)
11 Guard (7)
13 Believe (5)
14 Shun (5)
16 Conifer (3)
18 Bore (7)
21 God (5)
22 Accustom (5)
24 Hermit (7)
27 Obese (3)
28 Sampled (6)
29 Place (5)
32 Stock (5)
33 Senior (5)
35 Devil (3)
36 Bowl (4)

18

ACROSS

1 Staunch (4)
4 Border (3)
6 Roguish (4)
8 Meander (6)
9 Hidden (6)
10 Rabbit (3)
12 Swift (5)
14 Thespian (5)
15 Jockey (5)
18 Display (6)
20 Combined (6)
24 Famous (5)
26 Ignominy (5)
28 Tired (5)
30 Aye (3)
32 Hypnotic state (6)
33 Pale (6)
34 Whirlpool (4)
35 Cover (3)
36 Pull (4)

DOWN

2 Head-dress (5)
3 Wine (7)
4 Difficult (4)
5 Masculine (4)
6 Garret (5)
7 Comfort (7)
11 Poem (3)
12 Tear (3)
13 Performed (3)
16 Lair (3)
17 Groove (3)
19 Stuck (7)
21 Novel (3)
22 Perfectly (7)
23 Parched (3)
25 Mineral (3)
27 Cash (5)
29 Rule (5)
30 Shout (4)
31 Rushed (4)

Evening Standard

19

ACROSS

1 Shrewd (6)
5 Calamitous (6)
8 Of late (8)
9 Jump (4)
10 Spring (3)
12 Flavour (5)
15 Stitch (3)
17 For each (3)
18 Pinch (3)
19 Sleep (3)
20 Precise (5)
21 Spike (3)
22 Meadow (3)
23 Epoch (3)
24 Watch (3)
26 Giver (5)
29 Lock-opener (3)
33 Conceited (4)
34 Soak (8)
35 Purpose (6)
36 Outcome (6)

DOWN

2 Precipitous (5)
3 Employed (4)
4 Additional (5)
5 Rendezvous (5)
6 Competent (4)
7 Angry (5)
10 Because (5)
11 Fruit (5)
12 Trample (5)
13 Blemish (5)
14 Go in (5)
15 Utter (5)
16 Fret (5)
25 Long (5)
27 Attack (5)
28 Exterior (5)
30 Laud (5)
31 Formerly (4)
32 Dagger (4)

20

ACROSS

- **1** Cease (4)
- **4** Mouthful (3)
- **6** Pace (4)
- **9** Enclosure (3)
- **10** Perpetual (8)
- **11** Nobleman (4)

14 Encountered (3)
16 Grown-up (5)
19 Stated (8)
21 Singer (4)
23 Destroy (8)
24 Fear (5)
27 Bird (3)
31 Donkey (4)

33 Originated (8)
34 Transgression (3)
35 Pip (4)
36 Owing (3)
37 Informed (4)

DOWN

- **2** Implement (4)
- **3** Plague (4)
- **4** Drooled (8)
- **5** Compassion (4)
- **6** Pass (5)
- **7** Beverage (3)

8 Enlist (5)
12 Bordered (5)
13 Twenty (5)
14 Rug (3)
15 Principle (5)
17 Unfastened (5)
18 Taut (5)
20 Rule (8)
22 Decay (3)

25 Excite (5)
26 Correct (5)
28 Eat (4)
29 Hypocrisy (4)
30 Repast (4)
32 Untruth (3)

Evening Standard

21

ACROSS

- **4** Waterway (5)
- **7** Excited (6)
- **9** Record (3)
- **10** Whelp (3)
- **12** Fire-raising (5)
- **13** Pour (4)
- **15** Packing-case (5)
- **17** Physician (6)
- **19** Cheese (4)
- **20** Track (5)
- **22** Vigour (3)
- **24** Determined (7)
- **27** Lump (3)
- **28** Upright (5)
- **31** Rage (4)
- **33** Reposed (6)
- **35** View (5)
- **37** Testament (4)
- **38** Lariat (5)
- **39** Faucet (3)
- **41** Tune (3)
- **42** Sullen (6)
- **43** Gem (5)

DOWN

- **1** Free (6)
- **2** Dinner-jacket (6)
- **3** Vitality (3)
- **4** Cover (4)
- **5** Concur (5)
- **6** Spicy-smelling (8)
- **8** Tube (4)
- **11** Frugal (9)
- **14** Humour (4)
- **16** Parched (4)
- **18** Gang (4)
- **21** Masses (8)
- **23** Encounter (4)
- **25** Attention (4)
- **26** Sketched (4)
- **29** Reviser (6)
- **30** Cashier (6)
- **32** Composition (5)
- **34** Join (4)
- **36** Spiral (4)
- **40** Seed-case (3)

22

ACROSS

3 Mug (6)
5 Base (6)
9 Broader (5)
10 Assisted (6)
11 Share (6)
12 Spree (5)
14 Cook slowly (4)
17 Rodent (3)
18 Egg-shaped (4)
20 Subject (5)
22 Riddle (5)
23 Thorough-going (7)
24 Stitched (5)
26 Lukewarm (5)
29 Poke (4)
30 Pull (3)
32 Dandy (4)
33 Fundamental (5)
35 Trial (6)
36 Coarse (6)
37 Wanderer (5)
38 Soup-dish (6)
39 Sewing-aid (6)

DOWN

1 Command (6)
2 Slumbering (6)
3 Pitcher (4)
4 Jockey (5)
5 Cap (5)
6 Spoken (4)
7 Steal (6)
8 Mutilate (6)
13 Divers (7)
15 Soar (5)
16 Cabled (5)
18 Lubricated (5)
19 Shun (5)
21 Rotter (3)
22 Posed (3)
24 Shoot (6)
25 Awe (6)
27 Cleansed (6)
28 Order (6)
30 Claw (5)
31 Donated (5)
33 Naked (4)
34 Remedy (4)

Evening Standard

23

ACROSS

3 Fluctuate (5)
9 Trundled (6)
10 Soaked (6)
11 Curtain (5)
12 Bearing (4)
15 Delicate (4)
17 Memory-loss (7)
20 Sailor (3)
21 Weary (5)
23 Imitated (4)
25 Trial (4)
26 Sovereign (5)
28 Fixed (3)
30 Merit (7)
33 Revise (4)
35 Stagger (4)
36 Helped (5)
38 Infuriate (6)
39 Sweet (6)
40 Bordered (5)

DOWN

1 Play (5)
2 Stranger (5)
3 Married (3)
4 Skilful (6)
5 Notice (4)
6 Fish-eggs (3)
7 Confess (5)
8 Beneath (5)
13 Transfixed (7)
14 Not ever (5)
16 Prisoner (7)
18 Pointed (5)
19 Favourite (3)
22 Dissuade (5)
24 Owing (3)
27 Ebb (6)
28 Drain (5)
29 Head-dress (5)
31 Attain (5)
32 Chosen (5)
34 Expired (4)
36 Era (3)
37 Defective (3)

24

ACROSS

1 Straight (6)
5 Swarthy (4)
8 Staid (5)
9 Edge (3)
10 Prophet (4)
11 Scrutinise (4)
12 Era (5)

13 Motorist (6)
16 Rip (4)
18 Standard (4)
20 Through (3)
22 Freeze (3)
23 Attempt (3)
24 Season (4)
25 Tidy (4)
28 Reptile (6)

30 Storehouse (5)
32 Peruse (4)
33 Thoroughfare (4)
34 Wrath (3)
35 Respond (5)
36 Generated (4)
37 Passionate (6)

DOWN

1 Scorn (6)
2 Stayed (8)
3 Pamper (6)
4 Physical (9)
5 Fall (7)
6 Roguish (4)
7 Sort (4)

8 Observe (3)
14 Strengthen (9)
15 Snoop (3)
17 Expert (3)
19 Arrange (8)
20 Mine (3)
21 Ebbed (7)
26 Firewood (6)
27 Coming (6)

29 Snatch (4)
30 Challenge (4)
31 Child (3)

Evening Standard

25

ACROSS

1 Principal (5)
5 Sun-bathed (6)
8 House (5)
10 Stick (6)
11 Part (4)
14 Excavate under water (6)

DOWN

2 Concealed (3)
3 Smoothly (6)
4 Conifer (3)
5 Poet (4)
6 Quiet (6)
7 Erase (6)
9 Lawfully (7)

15 Deceive (7)
18 Finish (3)
19 Throw (3)
21 Sort (4)
23 Passage (5)
24 Cut (4)
27 Longing (3)
29 Obscure (3)
31 Charm (7)

12 Mineral (3)
13 Whirlpool (4)
16 Goat (4)
17 Distributed (5)
20 Advantage (7)
22 Track (4)
24 Harmony (6)
25 Paradise (4)
26 God-like (6)

32 Talented (6)
34 Number (4)
35 Stupidity (6)
38 Famous (5)
39 Loathe (6)
40 Poor (5)

28 Separate (6)
30 Males (3)
33 Hire-charge (4)
36 Lair (3)
37 Fish (3)

26

ACROSS

2 Feeling (5)
7 Pain (4)
8 Reveal (6)
9 Horrify (5)
11 Vehicle (3)
13 Colour (3)
15 Top (4)

DOWN

1 Fragment (5)
2 Ocean (3)
3 Pinch (3)
4 Fish (3)
5 Imitate (3)
6 Advantage (5)
10 So be it (4)

16 For each (3)
18 Tardy (4)
19 Signified (7)
20 Declare (4)
22 Cultivate (4)
23 Doubtful (7)
25 Paradise (4)
27 Untruth (3)
28 Divide (4)

11 Body (7)
12 Ebbed (7)
13 Fundamental (7)
14 Exhaust (7)
16 Danger (5)
17 Rascal (5)
18 Permit (3)
21 Manage (3)

30 Clear (3)
31 Shelter (3)
33 Nest (5)
36 Picture-house (6)
37 Attack (4)
38 Jockey (5)

24 Greasy (4)
26 Number (5)
29 Send (5)
32 Fixed (3)
33 Spike (3)
34 Wand (3)
35 Stray (3)

Evening Standard ═══

27

ACROSS

2 Discourage (5)
7 Swift (5)
8 Sound (5)
10 Famous (5)
12 Nothing (3)
13 Cringe (5)
15 Discussed (7)
17 Peruser (6)
19 Fruit (3)
20 Determined (7)
23 Fastened (4)
25 Barrel (4)
26 Withdrew (7)
30 Vehicle (3)
31 Audacious (6)
34 Knocked down (7)
37 Sprite (5)
38 Consume (3)
39 Evade (5)
40 Cap (5)
41 Elicit (5)
42 Grandeur (5)

DOWN

1 Boat (5)
2 Ate (5)
3 Worshipped (6)
4 Require (4)
5 Ran (7)
6 Heaped (5)
9 Illuminated (3)
11 Polluted (7)
13 Packing-case (5)
14 Irrigate (5)
16 Offer (3)
18 Purified (7)
21 Sewer (5)
22 Likeness (5)
24 Dedicated (7)
27 Sailor (3)
28 Dirk (6)
29 Slumber (5)
32 Shrill (5)
33 Relation (5)
35 Scull (3)
36 Puppet (4)

28

ACROSS

1 Prima donna (4)
4 Massage (3)
6 Ill (4)
8 Shut (6)
9 Shouted (6)
10 Moose (3)

12 Cash (5)
14 Memorise (5)
15 Royal (5)
18 Erase (6)
20 Speaker (6)
24 Sum (5)
26 Mar (5)
28 Parrot (5)
30 Artful (3)

32 Devastate (6)
33 Fur (6)
34 Formerly (4)
35 Faucet (3)
36 Dunce (4)

DOWN

2 Ice-house (5)
3 Harsh (7)
4 Travel (4)
5 Support (4)
6 Ointment (5)
7 Goodbye (7)
11 Meadow (3)

12 Insane (3)
13 Still (3)
16 Obtain (3)
17 Fate (3)
19 Elucidate (7)
21 Butt (3)
22 Frightened (7)
23 Uncooked (3)
25 Lubricate (3)

27 Angry (5)
29 Cancel (5)
30 Chair (4)
31 Yap (4)

Evening Standard ══════

29

ACROSS

1 Away (6)
5 Beat (6)
8 Substance (8)
9 Mislaid (4)
10 Damp (3)
12 Allude (5)
15 Finish (3)
17 Wrath (3)
18 Objective (3)
19 Epoch (3)
20 Fool (5)
21 Ban (3)
22 Mat (3)
23 Watch (3)
24 Vegetable (3)
26 Nude (5)
29 Regret (3)
33 Penalty (4)
34 Intense (8)
35 Plague (6)
36 Athlete (6)

DOWN

2 Censure (5)
3 Flat (4)
4 Banal (5)
5 Dig (5)
6 Tumbled (4)
7 Fire-raising (5)
10 Pup (5)
11 Head-dress (5)
12 Rule (5)
13 Frolic (5)
14 Assessed (5)
15 Cinder (5)
16 Lament (5)
25 Chosen (5)
27 Change (5)
28 Mistake (5)
30 Combine (5)
31 Warmth (4)
32 Bearing (4)

30

ACROSS

1 Staunch (4)
4 Cur (3)
6 Duty (4)
9 Everything (3)
10 Subside (8)
11 Carry (4)
14 Deed (3)
16 Flat (5)
19 Deviser (8)
21 Principle (5)
23 Decrease (8)
24 Deposit (5)
27 Top (3)
31 Spouse (4)
33 Tepid (8)
34 Strive (3)
35 Crowd (4)
36 Evil (3)
37 Curse (4)

DOWN

2 Implement (4)
3 Masculine (4)
4 Portrayed (8)
5 Mirth (4)
6 List (5)
7 Beer (3)
8 Quench (5)
12 Essential (5)
13 Shun (5)
14 Insect (3)
15 Pick-me-up (5)
17 Call (5)
18 Supple (5)
20 Observed (8)
22 Gratuity (3)
25 Fruit (5)
26 Avarice (5)
28 Cudgel (4)
29 Mop (4)
30 Press (4)
32 Conifer (3)

Evening Standard

31

ACROSS

4 Form (5)
7 Firework (6)
9 Ocean (3)
10 Golf-peg (3)
12 Mistake (5)
13 Pour (4)
15 Incline (5)

17 Insolvent (6)
19 Temper (4)
20 View (5)
22 Sleep (3)
24 Hung (7)
27 Beverage (3)
28 Prompt (5)
31 Go by (4)
33 Said (6)

35 Skinflint (5)
37 List (4)
38 Quilt (5)
39 Obscure (3)
41 Limb (3)
42 Erase (6)
43 Kingdom (5)

DOWN

1 Free (6)
2 Consent (6)
3 Damp (3)
4 Ooze (4)
5 Seraglio (5)
6 Advanced (8)
8 Trial (4)

11 Stretched (9)
14 Repair (4)
16 Spoken (4)
18 Defeat (4)
21 Being (8)
23 Saucy (4)
25 Headland (4)
26 Caribou (4)

29 Worshipped (6)
30 Shouted (6)
32 Odour (5)
34 Parched (4)
36 Detail (4)
40 Males (3)

32

ACROSS

1 Really (6)
5 Bred (6)
9 Legally acceptable (5)
10 Wood (6)
11 Talented (6)
12 Send (5)
14 Clothed (4)
17 Performed (3)
18 Yield (4)
20 Principle (5)
22 Managed (5)
23 Thief (7)
24 Bird (5)
26 Singer (5)
29 One (4)
30 Married (3)
32 Sand-hill (4)
33 Hell (5)
35 Thought (6)
36 Mend (6)
37 Lawful (5)
38 Raved (6)
39 Annually (6)

DOWN

1 Whole (6)
2 Debase (6)
3 Always (4)
4 Challenged (5)
5 Inflexible (5)
6 Revise (4)
7 Sooner (6)
8 Evaded (6)
13 Mixed (7)
15 Fruit (5)
16 Liability (5)
18 Bothered (5)
19 Devil (5)
21 Cask (3)
22 Obese (3)
24 Athlete (6)
25 Nipped (6)
27 Figure (6)
28 Cure (6)
30 Declined (5)
31 Rot (5)
33 Cavity (4)
34 Only (4)

Evening Standard ═══

33

ACROSS

3 Jam (5)
9 Decayed (6)
10 Gorge (6)
11 Sea-duck (5)
12 Sinful (4)
15 Sapient (4)
17 Given (7)
20 Deed (3)
21 Ate (5)
23 Company (4)
25 Inform (4)
26 Allude (5)
28 Fixed (3)
30 Renewed (7)
33 Region (4)
35 Season (4)
36 Funny (5)
38 Bird (6)
39 Cunning (6)
40 Malice (5)

DOWN

1 Generate (5)
2 Blemish (5)
3 Tiny (3)
4 Revised (6)
5 Increased (4)
6 Spike (3)
7 Shinbone (5)
8 Beleaguer (5)
13 Docket (7)
14 Subsequently (5)
16 Berated (7)
18 Frogman (5)
19 Obtain (3)
22 Outcoming (5)
24 Network (3)
27 Oppose (6)
28 Relish (5)
29 Instruct (5)
31 Hazy (5)
32 Dissuade (5)
34 Cage (4)
36 Lettuce (3)
37 Hint (3)

34

ACROSS

1 Each (6)
5 Soon (4)
8 Barrier (5)
9 Child (3)
10 Pitcher (4)
11 Arrived (4)
12 Anaesthetic (5)

13 Vegetable (6)
16 Gull (4)
18 Discharge (4)
20 Wicked (3)
22 Prosecute (3)
23 Defective (3)
24 Masculine (4)
25 Marquee (4)
28 Nursed (6)

30 Fashion (5)
32 Curdle (4)
33 Orient (4)
34 Fish-eggs (3)
35 Coin (5)
36 Act (4)
37 Span (6)

DOWN

1 Shrewd (6)
2 Within (8)
3 Believe (6)
4 Apposite (9)
5 Consented (7)
6 Close (4)
7 Require (4)

8 Charge (3)
14 Pernicious (9)
15 Cover (3)
17 Regret (3)
19 Killed (8)
20 Bight (3)
21 Relegated (7)
26 Examiner (6)
27 Stick (6)

29 Tart (4)
30 Be gloomy (4)
31 Age (3)

Evening Standard

35

ACROSS

1 Embrace (5)
5 Yawning (6)
8 Keen (5)
10 Scold (6)
11 Press (4)
14 Part (6)
15 Officer (7)

DOWN

2 Untruth (3)
3 Tide (6)
4 Tap (3)
5 Grid (4)
6 Demonstrated (6)
7 Festivity (6)

18 Enclosure (3)
19 Free (3)
21 Flout (4)
23 Noted (5)
24 Peruse (4)
27 Rim (3)
29 Vigour (3)
31 Torment (7)
32 Talented (6)

9 Widespread (7)
12 Tear (3)
13 Number (4)
16 Formerly (4)
17 Confine (5)
20 Ousted (7)
22 Dread (4)
24 Disc (6)

34 Ceremony (4)
35 Coarse (6)
38 Elbow (5)
39 Summary (6)
40 Bordered (5)

25 Swear (4)
26 God-like (6)
28 Stocked (6)
30 Encountered (3)
33 Hire (4)
36 Era (3)
37 Colour (3)

36

ACROSS

2 Laud (5)
7 Knife (4)
8 Shrewd (6)
9 Plank (5)
11 Defective (3)
13 Brick-carrier (3)

15 Detail (4)
16 Summit (3)
18 Heap (4)
19 Observed (7)
20 Jetty (4)
22 Harvest (4)
23 Twisted (7)
25 Pour (4)
27 Concealed (3)

28 Rotate (4)
30 Finish (3)
31 Mournful (3)
33 Cut (5)
36 Devalue (6)
37 Group (4)
38 Flinch (5)

DOWN

1 Portly (5)
2 Recede (3)
3 Beverage (3)
4 Youth (3)
5 Pig-pen (3)
6 Seat (5)
10 Foundation (4)

11 Argument (7)
12 Erased (7)
13 Ghastly (7)
14 Despair (7)
16 Leathery (5)
17 Longed (5)
18 For each (3)
21 Butt (3)
24 Similar (4)

26 Go in (5)
29 Wild (5)
32 Pale (3)
33 Stitch (3)
34 Vehicle (3)
35 Regret (3)

Evening Standard ═══

37

ACROSS

2 Condition (5)
7 Wireless (5)
8 Demon (5)
10 Weary (5)
12 Loiter (3)
13 Pattern (5)
15 Relegated (7)
17 Worn (6)
19 Obese (3)
20 Exhausted (7)
23 Require (4)
25 Expensive (4)
26 Discussed (7)
30 Edge (3)
31 Erase (6)
34 Made (7)
37 Bothered (5)
38 Managed (3)
39 Send (5)
40 Mix (5)
41 Thick (5)
42 Guide (5)

DOWN

1 Greater (5)
2 Located (5)
3 Laboured (6)
4 Fastened (4)
5 Flew (7)
6 Wrath (5)
9 Consume (3)
11 Polluted (7)
13 Intended (5)
14 Drugged (5)
16 Male (3)
18 Visionary (7)
21 Dissuade (5)
22 Avarice (5)
24 Madden (7)
27 Nipped (3)
28 Determine (6)
29 Strayed (5)
32 Subsequently (5)
33 Taut (5)
35 Spike (3)
36 Adroit (4)

38

ACROSS

1 Fashionable (4)
4 Cur (3)
6 Settled (4)
8 Betrothed (6)
9 Whole (6)
10 Immerse (3)
12 Endured (5)
14 Near (5)
15 Wrinkled (5)
18 Maintain (6)
20 Tell (6)
24 Broader (5)
26 Scoff (5)
28 Principle (5)
30 Beer (3)
32 Purchasing (6)
33 Austerity (6)
34 Inactive (4)
35 Owing (3)
36 Row (4)

DOWN

2 Raise (5)
3 Comfort (7)
4 Act (4)
5 Grasp (4)
6 Leaf (5)
7 Tooth (7)
11 Wrath (3)
12 Spring (3)
13 Delve (3)
16 Novel (3)
17 Performed (3)
19 Drooping (7)
21 Entrap (3)
22 Cargo (7)
23 Rug (3)
25 Sick (3)
27 Chosen (5)
29 Ooze (5)
30 Elderly (4)
31 Sea-eagle (4)

Evening Standard

39

| | | | | | | | | |
|1|2| |3| |4| |5| |6| |7| | |

ACROSS

1 Sterile (6)
5 Filter (6)
8 Gently (8)
9 Rip (4)
10 Ban (3)
12 Beleaguer (5)
15 Fixed (3)
17 Lubricate (3)
18 Fish-eggs (3)
19 Beam (3)
20 Delete (5)
21 Expert (3)
22 Donkey (3)
23 Objective (3)
24 Fish (3)
26 War-horse (5)
29 Still (3)
33 Employed (4)
34 Soften (8)
35 Confused (6)
36 Debase (6)

DOWN

2 Stadium (5)
3 Travel (4)
4 Courage (5)
5 Mode (5)
6 Ceremony (4)
7 Angry (5)
10 Canal-boat (5)
11 Regal (5)
12 Consecrate (5)
13 Form (5)
14 Trample (5)
15 Sordid (5)
16 Handle (5)
25 Relaxed (5)
27 Domesticated (5)
28 Finished (5)
30 Additional (5)
31 Image (4)
32 Terrible (4)

40

ACROSS

1 Drop (4)
4 Beaker (3)
6 Impetuous (4)
9 Sicken (3)
10 Length (8)
11 Thought (4)
14 Mire (3)

16 Jumped (5)
19 Dead (8)
21 Allude (5)
23 Stripping (8)
24 Tendency (5)
27 Decay (3)
31 Discourteous (4)
33 Persuade (8)

34 Turf (3)
35 Repudiate (4)
36 Expire (3)
37 Dregs (4)

DOWN

2 Greedy (4)
3 Tardy (4)
4 Bewildered (8)
5 Nobleman (4)
6 Elevate (5)
7 Help (3)
8 Slumber (5)

12 Confess (5)
13 View (5)
14 Spoil (3)
15 Postpone (5)
17 Garret (5)
18 Colour (5)
20 Condemn (8)
22 Groove (3)
25 Excite (5)

26 Poor (5)
28 Tart (4)
29 Murder (4)
30 Pain (4)
32 Fellow (3)

Evening Standard

41

ACROSS

4 Stub (5)
7 Attacker (6)
9 Because (3)
10 Summit (3)
12 Lariat (5)
13 Grave (4)
15 Broom (5)
17 Detain (6)
19 Act (4)
20 Boat (5)
22 Gratuity (3)
24 Hesitated (7)
27 Equality (3)
28 Wanderer (5)
31 Cab (4)
33 Small (6)
35 View (5)
37 Sea-eagle (4)
38 House (5)
39 Breach (3)
41 Epoch (3)
42 Decline (6)
43 Combine (5)

DOWN

1 Amatory (6)
2 Aviator (6)
3 Fixed (3)
4 Unaccompanied (4)
5 Vagrant (5)
6 Carnage (8)
8 Gown (4)
11 Plaguing (9)
14 Forehead (4)
16 Agitate (4)
18 Harvest (4)
21 Dog (8)
23 Saucy (4)
25 Valley (4)
26 Distribute (4)
29 Against (6)
30 Staggered (6)
32 Island (5)
34 Rip (4)
36 Attention (4)
40 Enclosure (3)

42

ACROSS

- **1** Respect (6)
- **5** Slender (6)
- **9** Weird (5)
- **10** Method (6)
- **11** Race (6)
- **12** Drugged (5)
- **14** Always (4)
- **17** Novel (3)
- **18** Present (4)
- **20** Jockey (5)
- **22** Pattern (5)
- **23** Drawing (7)
- **24** Portly (5)
- **26** Beleaguer (5)
- **29** Couple (4)
- **30** Cover (3)
- **32** Dreadful (4)
- **33** Of sound (5)
- **35** Combined (6)
- **36** Bit (6)
- **37** Heron (5)
- **38** Motor (6)
- **39** Guard (6)

DOWN

- **1** Rota (6)
- **2** Panted (6)
- **3** Rush (4)
- **4** Devil (5)
- **5** Tendon (5)
- **6** Guide (4)
- **7** Profited (6)
- **8** Burrow (6)
- **13** Belong (7)
- **15** View (5)
- **16** Happen again (5)
- **18** Sharpened (5)
- **19** Allude (5)
- **21** Rodent (3)
- **22** Crowd (3)
- **24** Trim (6)
- **25** Lubricating (6)
- **27** Easy (6)
- **28** Nursed (6)
- **30** Deposit (5)
- **31** Ate (5)
- **33** Observed (4)
- **34** Quote (4)

Evening Standard

43

ACROSS

3 Last (5)
9 Rouse (6)
10 Disappear (6)
11 Moral (5)
12 Flag (4)
15 Pit (4)
17 Fall (7)

20 Bed (3)
21 Old-fashioned (5)
23 Divide (4)
25 Fairy (4)
26 Consumed (5)
28 Insect (3)
30 Harmed (7)
33 Image (4)

35 Travel (4)
36 Inflexible (5)
38 Involve (6)
39 Seller (6)
40 Twelve (5)

DOWN

1 Swift (5)
2 Foundation (5)
3 Charge (3)
4 Mean (6)
5 Greedy (4)
6 Resin (3)
7 Municipal (5)

8 Pane (5)
13 Reply (7)
14 Frighten (5)
16 Observed (7)
18 Domesticated (5)
19 Material (3)
22 Exclude (5)
24 Brown (3)

27 Inherent (6)
28 Helped (5)
29 Molar (5)
31 Dizzy (5)
32 Disparage (5)
34 Grain-store (4)
36 Free (3)
37 Lair (3)

44

ACROSS

1 Abrade (6)
5 Adroit (4)
8 Pointed (5)
9 Lettuce (3)
10 Deficit (4)
11 Sense (4)
12 Blemish (5)

13 Give (6)
16 Sea-bird (4)
18 Discharge (4)
20 Marry (3)
22 Cushion (3)
23 Immerse (3)
24 Broad (4)
25 Pitcher (4)
28 Trader (6)

30 Artery (5)
32 Diplomacy (4)
33 Pain (4)
34 Bite (3)
35 Intended (5)
36 Require (4)
37 Dread (6)

DOWN

1 Safe (6)
2 Disliked (8)
3 Chicken (6)
4 Swelled (9)
5 Polluted (7)
6 Paradise (4)
7 Story (4)

8 Donkey (3)
14 Contrite (9)
15 Tear (3)
17 Uncooked (3)
19 Hat-seller (8)
20 Toupee (3)
21 Dedicated (7)
26 Ebb (6)
27 Decent (6)

29 Stupefy (4)
30 Summit (4)
31 Deed (3)

Evening Standard

45

ACROSS

1 Explosion (5)
5 Pill (6)
8 Madness (5)
10 Summer-house (6)
11 Bellow (4)
14 Character (6)
15 Deceive (7)
18 Colour (3)
19 Performed (3)
21 Tidy (4)
23 Stream (5)
24 Way out (4)
27 Rotter (3)
29 Speak (3)
31 Number (7)
32 Named (6)
34 Otherwise (4)
35 Deserved (6)
38 Elbow (5)
39 Pay (6)
40 Bordered (5)

DOWN

2 Meadow (3)
3 Stinking (6)
4 Tag (3)
5 Lake (4)
6 Defeated (6)
7 Gift (6)
9 Wandering (7)
12 Scull (3)
13 Discourteous (4)
16 Goat (4)
17 Couch (5)
20 Inferred (7)
22 Region (4)
24 Surpass (6)
25 Island (4)
26 Higher (6)
28 Scoffed (6)
30 Aye (3)
33 Repudiate (4)
36 Era (3)
37 Watch (3)

46

ACROSS

2 Principal (5)
7 Excuse (4)
8 Evoke (6)
9 Colour (5)
11 Rug (3)
13 Expire (3)
15 Soon (4)
16 Insane (3)
18 Stuff (4)
19 Train (7)
20 Caribou (4)
22 Lofty (4)
23 Curl (7)
25 Pour (4)
27 Spike (3)
28 Despatched (4)
30 Finish (3)
31 Rabbit (3)
33 Booth (5)
36 Reciprocal (6)
37 Declare (4)
38 Cede (5)

DOWN

1 Unsoiled (5)
2 Feline (3)
3 Tavern (3)
4 Charge (3)
5 Offer (3)
6 Shinbone (5)
10 Insect (4)
11 Instruction (7)
12 Soared (7)
13 Feared (7)
14 Imitate (7)
16 Combine (5)
17 Eater (5)
18 Sever (3)
21 Edge (3)
24 Continue (4)
26 Follow (5)
29 Famous (5)
32 Name (3)
33 Artful (3)
34 Expert (3)
35 Youth (3)

Evening Standard

47

ACROSS

2 New (5)
7 Gape (5)
8 Emulate (5)
10 Pungent (5)
12 Loiter (3)
13 Play (5)
15 Relegated (7)

17 Soften (6)
19 Posed (3)
20 Coach (7)
23 Due (4)
25 Expired (4)
26 Turned (7)
30 Entrap (3)
31 Pollute (6)
34 Creaked (7)

37 Yielded (5)
38 Skill (3)
39 Figure (5)
40 Brace (5)
41 Dissuade (5)
42 Stitched (5)

DOWN

1 Stock (5)
2 Structure (5)
3 Withdraw (6)
4 Slipped (4)
5 Flew (7)
6 Bet (5)
9 Tank (3)

11 Wished (7)
13 Sag (5)
14 Tree (5)
16 Male (3)
18 Handled (7)
21 Inflexible (5)
22 Bordered (5)
24 Gave (7)
27 Number (3)

28 Determine (6)
29 Hamper (5)
32 Entertained (5)
33 Bar (5)
35 Mineral (3)
36 Dreadful (4)

48

ACROSS

1 Record (4)
4 Summit (3)
6 Conceited (4)
8 Burrow (6)
9 Overseas (6)
10 Lair (3)
12 Liability (5)
14 Send (5)
15 Direction (5)
18 Scarce (6)
20 Entertained (6)
24 Fiend (5)
26 Exhausted (5)
28 Staff (5)
30 Firearm (3)
32 Mug (6)
33 Passionate (6)
34 Employed (4)
35 Fasten (3)
36 Challenge (4)

DOWN

2 Accustomed (5)
3 Sly (7)
4 Informed (4)
5 Scheme (4)
6 Edge (5)
7 Fancy (7)
11 Consume (3)
12 Obscure (3)
13 Hill (3)
16 Colour (3)
17 Meat (3)
19 State (7)
21 Crowd (3)
22 Unhelped (7)
23 Fellow (3)
25 Bird (3)
27 Nude (5)
29 Proprietor (5)
30 Courage (4)
31 Title (4)

Evening Standard

49

ACROSS

1 Worshipped (6)
5 Idiotic (6)
8 Example (8)
9 Inactive (4)
10 Shelter (3)
12 Spruce (5)
15 Deity (3)
17 Nothing (3)
18 Sick (3)
19 Deed (3)
20 Precise (5)
21 Imitate (3)
22 Watch (3)
23 Cover (3)
24 Sailor (3)
26 Fragment (5)
29 Tree (3)
33 Monster (4)
34 Month (8)
35 Dealer (6)
36 Required (6)

DOWN

2 Thick (5)
3 Speed (4)
4 Material (5)
5 Absolute (5)
6 One (4)
7 Ice-house (5)
10 Smallest (5)
11 Go in (5)
12 Slumber (5)
13 Astound (5)
14 Name (5)
15 Clearing (5)
16 Vision (5)
25 Wrath (5)
27 Deduce (5)
28 Hut (5)
30 Huge (5)
31 Guide (4)
32 Dumb (4)

50

ACROSS

1 Ooze (4)
4 Immerse (3)
6 Sapient (4)
9 Epoch (3)
10 Bragging (8)
11 Dale (4)
14 Ban (3)
16 Allude (5)
19 Believed (8)
21 Singer (5)
23 Signifying (8)
24 Attire (5)
27 Lump (3)
31 Delicate (4)
33 Original (8)
34 Prosecute (3)
35 Require (4)
36 Noise (3)
37 Humour (4)

DOWN

2 Uproar (4)
3 Over (4)
4 Beaten (8)
5 Tug (4)
6 Jam (5)
7 Wrath (3)
8 Ointment (5)
12 Performed (5)
13 Torment (5)
14 Nipped (3)
15 Renovate (5)
17 Feeble (5)
18 Scope (5)
20 Gift (8)
22 Wand (3)
25 Elevate (5)
26 Rate (5)
28 Rushed (4)
29 Staunch (4)
30 Unfasten (4)
32 Hint (3)

Evening Standard

51

ACROSS

4 Handle (5)
7 Canopy (6)
9 Sorrow (3)
10 Father (3)
12 Tender (5)
13 Dross (4)
15 Fabric (5)

DOWN

1 Mountain-peaks (6)
2 Unfold (6)
3 Plus (3)
4 Implement (4)
5 Allude (5)
6 Sufficient (8)

17 Meal (6)
19 Vanquish (4)
20 Untrue (5)
22 Mournful (3)
24 Cut (7)
27 Managed (3)
28 Consumed (5)
31 Lump (4)
33 Principal (6)

8 Fete (4)
11 Disagreed (9)
14 Muddle (4)
16 Asterisk (4)
18 Nobleman (4)
21 Promoted (8)
23 Intense (4)
25 Huge (4)
26 Valley (4)

35 Subsequently (5)
37 Comfort (4)
38 Ladle (5)
39 Immerse (3)
41 Favourite (3)
42 Erase (6)
43 Bordered (5)

29 Tormented (6)
30 Wanted (6)
32 Incline (5)
34 Parched (4)
36 Imitated (4)
40 Enclosure (3)

52

ACROSS

1 Suppose (6)
5 Grasp (6)
9 Follow (5)
10 Stumble (6)
11 Rue (6)
12 Soar (5)
14 Image (4)
17 Youth (3)
18 Pale (4)
20 Renovate (5)
22 Change (5)
23 Trace (7)
24 Enclosed (5)
26 Weird (5)
29 Spoken (4)
30 Tavern (3)
32 Informed (4)
33 Wrath (5)
35 Scarce (6)
36 Flower (6)
37 Crawl (5)
38 Snub (6)
39 Give (6)

DOWN

1 Matter (6)
2 Fish (6)
3 Encounter (4)
4 Enlist (5)
5 Remedied (5)
6 Ogle (4)
7 Gullet (6)
8 Here (6)
13 Absent (7)
15 Prevent (5)
16 Flat (5)
18 Swift (5)
19 Satan (5)
21 Married (3)
22 Era (3)
24 Deputy (6)
25 Sausage (6)
27 Revolved (6)
28 Reviser (6)
30 Inactive (5)
31 Not ever (5)
33 Cunning (4)
34 Mature (4)

Evening Standard

53

ACROSS

3 Garret (5)
9 Rest (6)
10 Harm (6)
11 Slumber (5)
12 Cupid (4)
15 Sapient (4)
17 Delineated (7)
20 Aged (3)
21 Inflexible (5)
23 Detail (4)
25 Support (4)
26 Old-fashioned (5)
28 Meadow (3)
30 Parted (7)
33 Inactive (4)
35 Naked (4)
36 Revolt (5)
38 Terrible (6)
39 Fondle (6)
40 God (5)

DOWN

1 Avarice (5)
2 Hoax (5)
3 Donkey (3)
4 Cashier (6)
5 Thought (4)
6 Beret (3)
7 Wireless (5)
8 Stitched (5)
13 Withdrew (7)
14 Located (5)
16 Smacked (7)
18 Plunged (5)
19 Gratuity (3)
22 Sewer (5)
24 Spoil (3)
27 Straight (6)
28 Supple (5)
29 Vigilant (5)
31 Cheated (5)
32 Thick (5)
34 Yield (4)
36 Free (3)
37 Ballad (3)

54

ACROSS

1 Leave (6)
5 Chair (4)
8 Elected (5)
9 Born (3)
10 Terrible (4)
11 Quote (4)
12 Asunder (5)
13 Feverish (6)
16 Observe (4)
18 Labour (4)
20 Ocean (3)
22 Entrap (3)
23 Stray (3)
24 Difficult (4)
25 Pour (4)
28 Submissive (6)
30 Stadium (5)
32 Govern (4)
33 One (4)
34 Sicken (3)
35 Advantage (5)
36 Stud (4)
37 Toyed (6)

DOWN

1 Boat (6)
2 Clergyman (8)
3 Recover (6)
4 Finished (9)
5 Hide (7)
6 Revise (4)
7 Fastened (4)
8 By way of (3)
14 Lasted (9)
15 Conifer (3)
17 Golf-peg (3)
19 Common (8)
20 Weaken (3)
21 Speech (7)
26 Human (6)
27 Shouted (6)
29 Snatch (4)
30 Unfortunately (4)
31 Insect (3)

Evening Standard ═══

55

ACROSS

1 Acute (5)
5 Method (6)
8 Passage (5)
10 Kindle (6)
11 Cheese (4)
14 Ripe (6)
15 Under (7)

DOWN

2 Pig (3)
3 Attacker (6)
4 Mine (3)
5 Appear (4)
6 Sitting (6)
7 Pester (6)
9 Colonist (7)

18 Still (3)
19 Cover (3)
21 Liability (4)
23 Cap (5)
24 Trial (4)
27 Colour (3)
29 Limb (3)
31 Obedient (7)
32 Invented (6)

12 Age (3)
13 Dumb (4)
16 Margin (4)
17 Leased (5)
20 Inferred (7)
22 Dandy (4)
24 Voucher (6)
25 Slipped (4)
26 Occupant (6)

34 Facts (4)
35 Sufficient (6)
38 Jockey (5)
39 Gossip (6)
40 Jam (5)

28 Previously (6)
30 Obtain (3)
33 Venture (4)
36 Novel (3)
37 Silence (3)

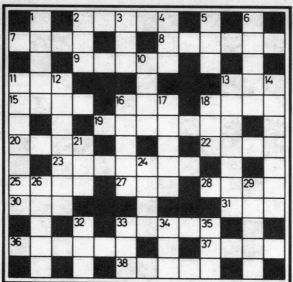

56

ACROSS

2 Vision (5)
7 Dandy (4)
8 Counting-frame (6)
9 Sketch (5)
11 Tune (3)
13 Everything (3)
15 Toboggan (4)
16 Help (3)
18 Nip (4)
19 Sorrowful (7)
20 Employer (4)
22 Self-satisfied (4)
23 Sale (7)
25 Comfort (4)
27 Skill (3)
28 Measure (4)
30 Expire (3)
31 Plaything (3)
33 Trap (5)
36 Purify (6)
37 Recognised (4)
38 Subject (5)

DOWN

1 Satan (5)
2 Defective (3)
3 Epoch (3)
4 Rug (3)
5 Beam (3)
6 Duvet (5)
10 Frustrate (4)
11 Certain (7)
12 Liberate (7)
13 Illness (7)
14 Long (7)
16 Artery (5)
17 Storehouse (5)
18 Coach (3)
21 Regret (3)
24 Press (4)
26 Intended (5)
29 Lid (5)
32 Mine (3)
33 Fixed (3)
34 Wonder (3)
35 Stretch (3)

Evening Standard

57

ACROSS

- **2** Grip (5)
- **7** Chaplain (5)
- **8** Dissuade (5)
- **10** Finished (5)
- **12** Vehicle (3)
- **13** Stitched (5)
- **15** Wished (7)
- **17** Exhilarated (6)
- **19** Cot (3)
- **20** Eased (7)
- **23** Prophet (4)
- **25** Dreadful (4)
- **26** Withdrew (7)
- **30** Vessel (3)
- **31** Slander (6)
- **34** Bracketed (7)
- **37** Lesser (5)
- **38** Consume (3)
- **39** Give (5)
- **40** Managed (5)
- **41** Torment (5)
- **42** Avarice (5)

DOWN

- **1** Tag (5)
- **2** Salute (5)
- **3** Give (6)
- **4** Rushed (4)
- **5** Determined (7)
- **6** Cap (5)
- **9** Sailor (3)
- **11** Discussed (7)
- **13** Feeling (5)
- **14** Irrigate (5)
- **16** Gender (3)
- **18** Delineated (7)
- **21** Couch (5)
- **22** Cut (5)
- **24** Famed (7)
- **27** Faucet (3)
- **28** Relegate (6)
- **29** Huge (5)
- **32** Discharged (5)
- **33** Elk (5)
- **35** Scull (3)
- **36** Entrance (4)

58

ACROSS

1 Cab (4)
4 Label (3)
6 Spoken (4)
8 Quicker (6)
9 Arouse (6)
10 Novel (3)
12 Between (5)

14 Ruse (5)
15 Shabby (5)
18 Delectable (6)
20 Team (6)
24 Consumed (5)
26 Composition (5)
28 Implicit (5)
30 Marry (3)

32 Oust (6)
33 Enrol (6)
34 Lake (4)
35 Cushion (3)
36 Sketched (4)

DOWN

2 Frighten (5)
3 Deep (7)
4 Ripped (4)
5 Increased (4)
6 Happen (5)
7 Thing (7)
11 Finish (3)

12 Sicken (3)
13 Solidify (3)
16 Watch (3)
17 Still (3)
19 Indecent (7)
21 Permit (3)
22 Empowered (7)
23 Entrap (3)

25 Imitate (3)
27 Over (5)
29 Outcome (5)
30 Cry (4)
31 Deceased (4)

Evening Standard

59

ACROSS

1 Platform (6)
5 Coma (6)
8 Wrong (8)
9 One (4)
10 Era (3)
12 Crawl (5)
15 Newt (3)

17 Pair (3)
18 Vase (3)
19 Record (3)
20 Bet (5)
21 Moose (3)
22 Sheep (3)
23 Jewel (3)
24 Lump (3)
26 Lament (5)

29 Longing (3)
33 Penalty (4)
34 Heaven (8)
35 Dog-house (6)
36 Deleted (6)

DOWN

2 Due (5)
3 Jot (4)
4 Manufacturer (5)
5 Taut (5)
6 Fever (4)
7 Principal (5)

10 Permit (5)
11 Bordered (5)
12 Intimidated (5)
13 Keen (5)
14 Cleanse (5)
15 Foe (5)
16 Symbol (5)
25 Similar (5)

27 Drive (5)
28 Furze (5)
30 Follow (5)
31 Observed (4)
32 Thought (4)

60

ACROSS

1 Staunch (4)
4 Pose (3)
6 Tart (4)
9 Wand (3)
10 Entertained (8)
11 Due (4)
14 Club (3)
16 Traded (5)
19 Telephonist (8)
21 Repulse (5)
23 Abandoned (8)
24 Jockey (5)
27 Colour (3)
31 Stop (4)
33 Hand-gun (8)
34 Golf-peg (3)
35 Ale (4)
36 Performed (3)
37 Scheme (4)

DOWN

2 Excursion (4)
3 Encounter (4)
4 Located (8)
5 Neat (4)
6 Ascended (5)
7 Intimidate (3)
8 Perfect (5)
12 Engine (5)
13 Foul (5)
14 Ban (3)
15 Drinker (5)
17 Sharp (5)
18 Late (5)
20 Reticent (8)
22 Guided (3)
25 Angry (5)
26 Go in (5)
28 Grating (4)
29 Applaud (4)
30 Nil (4)
32 Shelter (3)

Evening Standard

61

ACROSS

4 Waterway (5)
7 Assert (6)
9 Summit (3)
10 Material (3)
12 Tally (5)
13 Poke (4)
15 Not ever (5)
17 Decline (6)
19 Trial (4)
20 Dissuade (5)
22 Number (3)
24 Venerated (7)
27 Spike (3)
28 Fragrance (5)
31 Region (4)
33 Relative (6)
35 View (5)
37 Lament (4)
38 Lariat (5)
39 Jewel (3)
41 Epoch (3)
42 Mutilate (6)
43 Colourless (5)

DOWN

1 Panted (6)
2 Exertion (6)
3 Make a
   mistake (3)
4 Arrive (4)
5 Asunder (5)
6 Habituate (8)
8 Food-list (4)
11 Plaguing (9)
14 Caribou (4)
16 Swerve (4)
18 Liberate (4)
21 Intrude (8)
23 Tidy (4)
25 Urn (4)
26 Sketched (4)
29 Fruit (6)
30 Slumbering (6)
32 Advantage (5)
34 Appear (4)
36 Centre (4)
40 Insane (3)

62

ACROSS

1 Tumult (6)
5 Cigar (6)
9 Tree (5)
10 Stupidity (6)
11 Rural (6)
12 Hell (5)
14 Always (4)
17 Guided (3)
18 Oven (4)
20 Challenged (5)
22 Quietened (5)
23 Coped (7)
24 Inflexible (5)
26 Famous (5)
29 Revise (4)
30 Dined (3)
32 Certain (4)
33 Helped (5)
35 Pang (6)
36 Figure (6)
37 Unfastened (5)
38 Stubborn (6)
39 Simply (6)

DOWN

1 Combined (6)
2 Attacker (6)
3 Curved structure (4)
4 Regal (5)
5 Troubled (5)
6 Responsibility (4)
7 Clothes (6)
8 Rise (6)
13 Disfigured (7)
15 Sound (5)
16 Send (5)
18 Acclaim (5)
19 Bar (5)
21 Father (3)
22 Males (3)
24 Reposed (6)
25 Donating (6)
27 Fall (6)
28 Pay (6)
30 Demon (5)
31 Material (5)
33 Fever (4)
34 Dandy (4)

Evening Standard

63

ACROSS

3 Dispute (5)
9 Sullen (6)
10 Sex (6)
11 Oar (5)
12 Comfort (4)
15 Gala (4)
17 Arrange (7)
20 Colour (3)
21 Booth (5)
25 Rodents (4)
25 Expensive (4)
26 Refuge (5)
28 Finish (3)
30 Esteem (7)
33 Pace (4)
35 Row (4)
36 Den (5)
38 Flower (6)
39 Myth (6)
40 The Ram (5)

DOWN

1 Implant (5)
2 Coarse (5)
5 Donkey (3)
4 Niche (6)
5 Unsightly (4)
6 Fish (3)
7 Viper (5)
8 Avarice (5)
13 Illness (7)
14 Era (5)
16 Patio (7)
18 Anaesthetic (5)
19 Aged (3)
22 Jumped (5)
24 Consume (3)
27 Stylus (6)
28 Composition (5)
29 Prevent (5)
31 Sea-duck (5)
32 Deal (5)
34 Asterisk (4)
36 Ocean (3)
37 Aye (3)

64

ACROSS

1 Consent (6)
6 Platform (4)
8 Cut (5)
9 Wrath (3)
10 Dirt (4)
11 Wickedness (4)
12 Shy (5)

13 Feverish (6)
16 Attic (4)
18 Cheese (4)
20 Wand (3)
22 Sicken (3)
23 Performed (3)
24 Pit (4)
25 Increased (4)
28 Hang (6)

30 House (5)
32 Excuse (4)
33 Greedy (4)
34 Tune (3)
35 Condition (5)
36 Observe (4)
37 Pressing (6)

DOWN

1 Burning (6)
2 Compulsion (8)
3 Percolate (6)
4 Disparaged (9)
5 Invented (7)
6 Parched (4)
7 Staunch (4)

8 Pose (3)
14 Clot (9)
15 Mournful (3)
17 Conifer (3)
19 Shame (8)
20 Tear (3)
21 Digress (7)
26 Roam (6)
27 Rue (6)

29 Whirl (4)
30 Singlet (4)
31 Greeting (3)

Evening Standard

65

ACROSS

1 Handle (5)
5 Raised (6)
8 Emblem (5)
10 Appear (6)
11 Imitated (4)
14 Liking (6)
15 Desperation (7)

18 Still (3)
19 Vehicle (3)
21 Repose (4)
23 Mature (5)
24 Agitate (4)
27 Gratuity (3)
29 Pat (3)
31 Pliant (7)
32 Bird (6)

34 Swimming-pool (4)
35 Deserved (6)
38 Spoon (5)
39 Ebb (6)
40 Bordered (5)

DOWN

2 Strange (3)
3 Sudden (6)
4 Label (3)
5 Jump (4)
6 Antenna (6)
7 Flaw (6)
9 Loss (7)

12 Wages (3)
13 Fruit (4)
16 Discharge (4)
17 Swift (5)
20 Famed (7)
22 Vend (4)
24 Meal (6)
25 Image (4)
26 Gorge (6)

28 Stocked (6)
30 Cot (3)
33 Part (4)
36 Beer (3)
37 Watch (3)

66

ACROSS

2 Perfect (5)
7 Wicked (4)
8 Really (6)
9 Jumped (5)
11 Disencumber (3)
13 Help (3)

15 Revise (4)
16 Large (3)
18 Exempt (4)
19 Liberate (7)
20 One (4)
22 Facts (4)
23 Swelled (7)
25 Flat (4)
27 Sister (3)

28 Fever (4)
30 Performed (3)
31 Finish (3)
33 Rescued (5)
36 God-like (6)
37 Discharge (4)
38 Coach (5)

DOWN

1 Shun (5)
2 Sick (3)
3 Epoch (3)
4 Illuminated (3)
5 Append (3)
6 Weird (5)
10 Bucket (4)

11 Denied (7)
12 Parted (7)
13 Dispose (7)
14 Discussed (7)
16 Started (5)
17 Donated (5)
18 Ate (3)
21 Can (3)
24 Tunny (4)

26 Call (5)
29 Unfastened (5)
32 Intelligence (3)
33 Fixed (3)
34 By way of (3)
35 Lair (3)

Evening Standard

67

ACROSS

2 Loathe (5)
7 Shinbone (5)
8 Wall-painting (5)
10 Vision (5)
12 Rodent (3)
13 Drain (5)
15 Memorised (7)
17 Dealt (6)
19 Watch (3)
20 Swell (7)
23 Finished (4)
25 Threesome (4)
26 Relaxing (7)
30 Beverage (3)
31 Store (6)
34 Flood (7)
37 Poor (5)
38 Snake (3)
39 String (5)
40 Bring (5)
41 Elicit (5)
42 Harmony (5)

DOWN

1 Skinflint (5)
2 Helped (5)
3 Banned (6)
4 Spoken (4)
5 Stream (7)
6 Assessed (5)
9 Managed (3)
11 Assembly (7)
13 Seat (5)
14 Irrigate (5)
16 Always (3)
18 Remote (7)
21 Idler (5)
22 Wagon (5)
24 Withdraw (7)
27 Observe (3)
28 Sea-bird (6)
29 Dressed (5)
32 Shrill (5)
33 Order (5)
35 Decay (3)
36 Counterpart (4)

68

ACROSS

1 Fashionable (4)
4 Mine (3)
6 Support (4)
8 Method (6)
9 Lower (6)
10 Label (3)
12 Flat (5)
14 Access (5)
15 Respond (5)
18 Reel (6)
20 Speaker (6)
24 Giant (5)
26 Employees (5)
28 Broaden (5)
30 Cot (3)
32 Harm (6)
33 Counting-frame (6)
34 Shout (4)
35 Summit (3)
36 Pitcher (4)

DOWN

2 Pull (5)
3 Unison (7)
4 Divide (4)
5 Flavour (4)
6 Truncheon (5)
7 Goodbye (7)
11 Curve (3)
12 Fate (3)
13 Shelter (3)
16 Skill (3)
17 Child (3)
19 Affront (7)
21 Uncooked (3)
22 Enliven (7)
23 Manage (3)
25 Wrath (3)
27 Feeble (5)
29 Ooze (5)
30 Defeat (4)
31 Moist (4)

Evening Standard

69

ACROSS

1 Transgressor (6)
5 Needed (6)
8 Reverted (8)
9 Companion (4)
10 Consumed (3)
12 Cut (5)
15 Pouch (3)
17 Fruit (3)
18 Fish (3)
19 Youth (3)
20 Hatred (5)
21 Bird (3)
22 Stray (3)
23 Devil (3)
24 Sorrowful (3)
26 Upright (5)
29 Gratuity (3)
33 Penalty (4)
34 Buy (8)
35 Burrow (6)
36 Team (6)

DOWN

2 Unsuitable (5)
3 Intellect (4)
4 Scope (5)
5 Jam (5)
6 Title (4)
7 Additional (5)
10 Map-book (5)
11 Finished (5)
12 Stock (5)
13 Utter (5)
14 Send (5)
15 Slumbered (5)
16 Bunch (5)
25 Farewell (5)
27 Repulse (5)
28 Oath (5)
30 Outcome (5)
31 Intend (4)
32 Footwear item (4)

70

ACROSS

1 Grating (4)
4 Headgear (3)
6 Smack (4)
9 Vehicle (3)
10 Persuade (8)
11 Top (4)
14 Nipped (3)
16 Leaf (5)
19 Led (8)
21 Singer (5)
23 Abdicate (8)
24 Wanderer (5)
27 Label (3)
31 Formerly (4)
33 Original (8)
34 Dog (3)
35 Encounter (4)
36 Longing (3)
37 Duct (4)

DOWN

2 Space (4)
3 Plunge (4)
4 Contemplate (8)
5 Nobleman (4)
6 Frighten (5)
7 Circuit (3)
8 Stadium (5)
12 Reject (5)
13 Kingdom (5)
14 Wager (3)
15 Principle (5)
17 Stain (5)
18 Paramour (5)
20 Gift (8)
22 Steal (3)
25 Weight (5)
26 Deflect (5)
28 Nimble (4)
29 Cease (4)
30 Break (4)
32 Hint (3)

71

ACROSS

4 Conceit (5)
7 Pressed (6)
9 Observe (3)
10 Resin (3)
12 Scope (5)
13 Timber (4)
15 Subject (5)

17 Courteous (6)
19 Attention (4)
20 Wall-painting (5)
22 Stitch (3)
24 Hurried (7)
27 Spike (3)
28 Go sideways (5)

31 Minus (4)
33 Strain (6)
35 Portion (5)
37 Expensive (4)
38 Helped (5)
39 Faucet (3)
41 Tree (3)
42 Ordain (6)
43 Class (5)

DOWN

1 Tepee (6)
2 Hue (6)
3 Solidify (3)
4 Fairy (4)
5 Attain (5)
6 Nonsense verse (8)

8 Facts (4)
11 Inhibit (9)
14 Dingy (4)
16 Strip (4)
18 Depressed (4)
21 Hidden (8)
23 Direction (4)
25 Secure (4)
26 Expired (4)

29 Dismal (6)
30 Deserved (6)
32 Rate (5)
34 Precede (4)
36 Inactive (4)
40 Favourite (3)

72

ACROSS

1 Entangle (6)
5 Damaged (6)
9 Seeped (5)
10 Production (6)
11 Invoiced (6)
12 Refute (5)
14 Employer (4)
17 Illuminated (3)
18 Cavity (4)
20 Undress (5)
22 Drain (5)
23 Postponed (7)
24 Change (5)
26 Concur (5)
29 Rip (4)
30 Limb (3)
32 Deserve (4)
33 Fishing-basket (5)
35 Adviser (6)
36 Disagree (6)
37 Wanderer (5)
38 Bird (6)
39 Delectable (6)

DOWN

1 Departure (6)
2 Affair (6)
3 Tart (4)
4 Inn (5)
5 Outcoming (5)
6 Revise (4)
7 Candle-fat (6)
8 Totter (6)
13 Wierd (7)
15 Wrap (5)
16 Jockey (5)
18 Barrier (5)
19 Bar (5)
21 Through (3)
22 Ocean (3)
24 Nuclear (6)
25 Leather-worker (6)
27 Lottery (6)
28 Power (6)
30 Missile (5)
31 Decoration (5)
33 Cornet (4)
34 Swimming-pool (4)

Evening Standard

73

ACROSS

3 The Ram (5)
9 Funeral-car (6)
10 Tiny (6)
11 Blemish (5)
12 Mistake (4)
15 Front (4)
17 Stonework (7)
20 Fate (3)
21 Darkness (5)
23 Increased (4)
25 Gape (4)
26 Firearm (5)
28 Deity (3)
30 Exhausted (7)
33 Spoken (4)
35 Ripped (4)
36 Satan (5)
38 Emperor (6)
39 Tidier (6)
40 Quilt (5)

DOWN

1 Abyss (5)
2 Foundation (5)
3 Donkey (3)
4 Revert (6)
5 Discharge (4)
6 Transgress (3)
7 Rustic (5)
8 Cap (5)
13 Lassitude (7)
14 Might (5)
16 Oppose (7)
18 Cede (5)
19 Reserved (3)
22 Implicit (5)
24 Intelligence (3)
27 Fur (6)
28 Furze (5)
29 Dawdle (5)
31 Direction (5)
32 Disparage (5)
34 Food-list (4)
36 Father (3)
37 Permit (3)

74

ACROSS

1 Struggle (6)
5 Worry (4)
8 Assess (5)
9 Recede (3)
10 Bar (4)
11 Title (4)
12 Performed (5)

13 Courage (6)
16 Vend (4)
18 Unfortunately (4)
20 Network (3)
22 Beverage (3)
23 Ballad (3)
24 Manufactured (4)

25 Speed (4)
28 Die (6)
30 Advantage (5)
32 Ancestry (4)
33 Ballot (4)
34 Employ (3)
35 Command (5)
36 Row (4)
37 Thoroughfare (6)

DOWN

1 Deflect (6)
2 Mutinied (8)
3 Against (6)
4 Reckon (9)
5 Interment (7)
6 Peruse (4)
7 Pour (4)

8 By way of (3)
14 Recovered (9)
15 Wages (3)
17 Meadow (3)
19 Scope (8)
20 Pale (3)
21 Frenzied (7)
26 Anticipate (6)
27 Dislike (6)

29 Indistinct outline (4)
30 Soon (4)
31 Hill (3)

Evening Standard ═══════

75

ACROSS

1 Ruse (5)
5 Method (6)
8 Send (5)
10 Mad (6)
11 Detail (4)
14 Stay (6)
15 Demur (7)
18 Entrap (3)
19 Vase (3)
21 Flout (4)
23 Previous (5)
24 Clutch (4)
27 Consume (3)
29 Barrel (3)
31 Prosaic (7)
32 Dirty (6)
34 Memorandum (4)
35 Reviser (6)
38 Tree (5)
39 Stubborn (6)
40 Recently (5)

DOWN

2 Managed (3)
3 Cunning (6)
4 Knowledge (3)
5 Agitate (4)
6 Appeared (6)
7 Principally (6)
9 Step (7)
12 Number (3)
13 Companion (4)
16 Breed (4)
17 Ordeal (5)
20 Observed (7)
22 Insect (4)
24 Panted (6)
25 Related (4)
26 Pertain (6)
28 Withdraw (6)
30 Obtain (3)
33 Deceased (4)
36 Lair (3)
37 Lubricate (3)

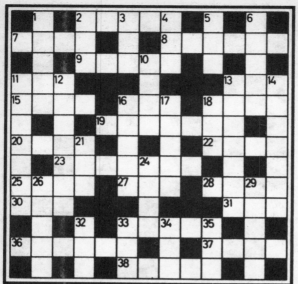

76

ACROSS

2 Unseeing (5)
7 Pain (4)
8 Uncertain (6)
9 Taut (5)
11 Rotter (3)
13 Tankard (3)
15 Candid (4)
16 Weep (3)
18 Couple (4)
19 Studio (7)
20 Bar (4)
22 Staunch (4)
23 Emptiness (7)
25 Munch (4)
27 Animal (3)
28 Ripped (4)
30 Hill (3)
31 Horse (3)
33 Brute (5)
36 Property (6)
37 Impel (4)
38 Verdant (5)

DOWN

1 Fragment (5)
2 Wager (3)
3 Tavern (3)
4 Owing (3)
5 Serpent (3)
6 Stream (5)
10 Footwear item (4)
11 Amend (7)
12 Liberate (7)
13 Share (7)
14 Pouring (7)
16 Wander (5)
17 Obstruction (5)
18 Aye (3)
21 Statute (3)
24 Title (4)
26 Dwelling (5)
29 Scope (5)
32 Ballad (3)
33 Entreat (3)
34 Wonder (3)
35 Cask (3)

Evening Standard ═══

77

ACROSS

2 Sea (5)
7 Stalk (5)
8 Change (5)
10 Clear (5)
12 Tune (3)
13 Advantage (5)
15 Exhausted (7)
17 Drawing (6)
19 Limb (3)
20 Lifted (7)
23 Always (4)
25 Eat (4)
26 Shortage (7)
30 Whim (3)
31 Rook (6)
34 Unaffected (7)
37 Stratum (5)
38 Child (3)
39 Cede (5)
40 Cringe (5)
41 Choose (5)
42 Wagon (5)

DOWN

1 Lively (5)
2 Bird (5)
3 Grasp (6)
4 Greedy (4)
5 Alleged (7)
6 Cap (5)
9 Can (3)
11 Severe (7)
13 Enquired (5)
14 Stitched (5)
16 Skill (3)
18 Vacation (7)
21 Soiled (5)
22 Cut (5)
24 Denied (7)
27 Distant (3)
28 Higher (6)
29 Staff (5)
32 Mournfully (5)
33 Blood-sucker (5)
35 Pull (3)
36 Swimming-pool (4)

78

ACROSS

1 Post (4)
4 Beaker (3)
6 Nail (4)
8 Thinner (6)
9 Innate (6)
10 Guided (3)
12 Trite (5)
14 Suspect (5)
15 Kind (5)
18 Erase (6)
20 Counting-frame (6)
24 Irrigate (5)
26 Extra (5)
28 Wilt (5)
30 Fixed (3)
32 Consign (6)
33 Haphazard (6)
34 Trial (4)
35 Doze (3)
36 Deserve (4)

DOWN

2 Stadium (5)
3 Ancestry (7)
4 Twist (4)
5 Rewarded (4)
6 Forbidden (5)
7 Deer (7)
11 Stray (3)
12 Wicked (3)
13 Permit (3)
16 Novel (3)
17 Consume (3)
19 Burst (7)
21 Cot (3)
22 Dispose (7)
23 Mouthful (3)
25 Expert (3)
27 Send (5)
29 Smell (5)
30 Stupefy (4)
31 Snare (4)

Evening Standard

ACROSS

1 Specimen (6)
5 Desired (6)
8 Landed (8)
9 Excursion (4)
10 Donkey (3)
12 Tag (5)

DOWN

2 Map-book (5)
3 Attendant (4)
4 Additional (5)
5 Jam (5)
6 Location (4)
7 Ooze (5)
10 Permit (5)

15 Encountered (3)
17 Fasten (3)
18 Poem (3)
19 Meadow (3)
20 Ate (5)
21 Sicken (3)
22 Mat (3)
23 Firearm (3)

11 Begin (5)
12 Shelf (5)
13 Premium (5)
14 Deposit (5)
15 Intended (5)
16 Agree (5)
25 Angry (5)
27 Elbow (5)
28 Spilt (5)

24 Intelligence (3)
26 Follow (5)
29 Plaything (3)
33 Chief (4)
34 Daunted (8)
35 Ebb (6)
36 Agreement (6)

30 Open (5)
31 Formerly (4)
32 Sport (4)

80

ACROSS

1 Detail (4)
4 Label (3)
6 Fall (4)
9 Steal from (3)
10 Keep (8)
11 Thought (4)
14 Posed (3)
16 Beleaguer (5)
19 Sheltered (8)
21 Cash (5)
23 Got (8)
24 Wireless (5)
27 Figure (3)
31 Quarrel (4)
33 Scatter (8)
34 Observe (3)
35 Ale (4)
36 Youth (3)
37 Soil (4)

DOWN

2 Rotate (4)
3 Overlook (4)
4 Bullfighter (8)
5 Increased (4)
6 Impel (5)
7 Wand (3)
8 Fat (5)
12 Moving (5)
13 Performed (5)
14 Amount (3)
15 Principle (5)
17 Serf (5)
18 Deal (5)
20 Dead (8)
22 Longing (3)
25 Originate (5)
26 Deduce (5)
28 Image (4)
29 Unite (4)
30 Employer (4)
32 Charge (3)

Evening Standard

81

ACROSS

4 Untrue (5)
7 Regard (6)
9 Unhappy (3)
10 Males (3)
12 Suspect (5)
13 Sinful (4)
15 Not ever (5)

17 Flood (6)
19 Paradise (4)
20 View (5)
22 Permit (3)
24 Wished (7)
27 Droop (3)
28 Called (5)
31 Lofty (4)
33 Sewing aid (6)

35 Correct (5)
37 Cheese (4)
38 Adhesive (5)
39 Gratuity (3)
41 Consume (3)
42 Pill (6)
43 Strict (5)

DOWN

1 Niche (6)
2 Pace (6)
3 Border (3)
4 Pale (4)
5 Worship (5)
6 Plunge (8)
8 Food-list (4)

11 Careless (9)
14 Loan (4)
16 Swerve (4)
18 Dregs (4)
21 Waterfall (8)
23 Nurse (4)
25 Sensible (4)
26 Valley (4)
29 Interfere (6)

30 Relegate (6)
32 Subsequently (5)
34 Revise (4)
36 Intend (4)
40 Wages (3)

82

ACROSS

1 Lottery (6)
5 Universal (6)
9 Of oats (5)
10 Fondle (6)
11 Real (6)
12 Short (5)
14 Rush (4)
17 Female animal (3)
18 Thin (4)
20 Old-fashioned (5)
22 Mournfully (5)
23 Shyness (7)
24 Storehouse (5)
26 Long (5)
29 Press (4)
30 Consumed (3)
32 Ceremony (4)
33 Demon (5)
35 Current (6)
36 Butted (6)
37 Singer (5)
38 Stuck (6)
39 Inclined (6)

DOWN

1 Disc (6)
2 Overlook (6)
3 Mislaid (4)
4 Relaxed (5)
5 Stop (5)
6 Formerly (4)
7 Manhandled (6)
8 Settlement (6)
13 Favour (7)
15 Keen (5)
16 Devil (5)
18 Stratum (5)
19 Vigilant (5)
21 Spot (3)
22 Pig-pen (3)
24 Fuel (6)
25 Teemed (6)
27 Aviators (6)
28 Wanted (6)
30 Pointed (5)
31 Enlist (5)
33 Destiny (4)
34 Venture (4)

Evening Standard

83

ACROSS

3 Devil (5)
9 Talented (6)
10 Guide (6)
11 Sharp (5)
12 Employed (4)
15 Sapient (4)
17 Withdrew (7)

20 Can (3)
21 Automaton (5)
23 Flat (4)
25 Record (4)
26 Lament (5)
28 Stitch (3)
30 Investigate (7)
33 Image (4)

35 Always (4)
36 Shinbone (5)
38 Hue (6)
39 Short (6)
40 Beleaguer (5)

DOWN

1 Scrub (5)
2 Cap (5)
3 Ocean (3)
4 Bowman (6)
5 Singer (4)
6 Born (3)
7 Confess (5)

8 Verdant (5)
13 Cut (7)
14 Ate (5)
16 Honest (7)
18 Evade (5)
19 Brick-carrier (3)
22 Name (5)
24 Nothing (3)

27 Tax (6)
28 Because (5)
29 Globe (5)
31 Open (5)
32 Made a mistake (5)
34 Weary (4)
36 Bath (3)
37 Deed (3)

84

ACROSS

1 Recent (6)
5 Yap (4)
8 Subdued (5)
9 Fate (3)
10 Anon (4)
11 Fever (4)
12 Frighten (5)

13 Motorist (6)
16 Expensive (4)
18 Pitcher (4)
20 Marry (3)
22 Trap (3)
23 Barrier (3)
24 Manufactured (4)
25 So be it (4)

28 Damaged (6)
30 Pale (5)
32 Beseech (4)
33 Jot (4)
34 Enemy (3)
35 Intended (5)
36 Expired (4)
37 Pill (6)

DOWN

1 Illness (6)
2 Enumerated (8)
3 Ventured (6)
4 Anxious (9)
5 Longed (7)
6 Rim (4)

7 Jetty (4)
8 Lettuce (3)
14 Recovering (9)
15 Jewel (3)
17 Purpose (3)
19 Extravagant (8)
20 Lump (3)
21 Rotten (7)

26 Deny (6)
27 Coming (6)
29 Rushed (4)
30 Repute (4)
31 Child (3)

Evening Standard

85

ACROSS

1 Slumbered (5)
5 Renew (6)
8 Shelf (5)
10 Placid (6)
11 Declare (4)
14 Harm (6)
15 Regulate (7)
18 Entrap (3)
19 Faucet (3)
21 Adroit (4)
23 Lawful (5)
24 Denomination (4)
27 Lair (3)
29 Epoch (3)
31 Behave violently (7)
32 Senior (6)
34 Simple (4)
35 Torment (6)
38 Iron (5)
39 Breakwater (6)
40 Trivial (5)

DOWN

2 Shelter (3)
3 Abundance (6)
4 Number (3)
5 Peruse (4)
6 Appeared (6)
7 Anticipate (6)
9 Relegated (7)
12 Vehicle (3)
13 Speed (4)
16 Exude (4)
17 Beer (5)
20 Swagger (7)
22 Standard (4)
24 Observing (6)
25 Yield (4)
26 Agreement (6)
28 Scanty (6)
30 Donkey (3)
33 Kind (4)
36 Serpent (3)
37 Fixed (3)

86

ACROSS

2 Inn (5)
7 Unaccompanied (4)
8 Bug (6)
9 Jig (5)
11 Lettuce (3)
13 Amount (3)
15 Loathe (4)
16 Whim (3)
18 Dreadful (4)
19 Unaffected (7)
20 Mud (4)
22 Ale (4)
23 Believed (7)
25 Prophet (4)
27 Consume (3)
28 Pain (4)
30 Finish (3)
31 Spike (3)
33 Art (5)
36 Ebb (6)
37 Candid (4)
38 Handle (5)

DOWN

1 Drink (5)
2 Brick-carrier (3)
3 Can (3)
4 Untruth (3)
5 Donkey (3)
6 Scrub (5)
10 Talk (4)
11 Shift (7)
12 Began (7)
13 Quiet (7)
14 Jollier (7)
16 Untrue (5)
17 Quilt (5)
18 Fish (3)
21 Be mistaken (3)
24 Vat (4)
26 Go in (5)
29 Hell (5)
32 Damp (3)
33 Fixed (3)
34 Wrath (3)
35 Fate (3)

Evening Standard

87

ACROSS

2 Lawful (5)
7 Unbend (5)
8 Lowed (5)
10 Guide (5)
12 Vase (3)
13 Elevate (5)
15 Theft (7)
17 Nut (6)
19 Bird (3)
20 Feared (7)
23 Watched (4)
25 Deceased (4)
26 Restricted (7)
30 Vehicle (3)
31 Scorn (6)
34 Lived (7)
37 Called (5)
38 Wicked (3)
39 Storehouse (5)
40 Gem (5)
41 Taut (5)
42 War-horse (5)

DOWN

1 Leaf (5)
2 Lariat (5)
3 Stretch (6)
4 Declare (4)
5 Suspected (7)
6 Kind (5)
9 Mineral (3)
11 Turned (7)
13 Ran (5)
14 Drive (5)
16 Offer (3)
18 Exhausted (7)
21 Material (5)
22 Bordered (5)
24 Parted (7)
27 Insane (3)
28 Signify (6)
29 Revolt (5)
32 Assessed (5)
33 Thick (5)
35 Noticed (3)
36 Adroit (4)

88

ACROSS

1 Present (4)
4 Mouthful (3)
6 Pour (4)
8 Botch (6)
9 Fisherman (6)
10 Snoop (3)
12 Utter (5)
14 Wander (5)
15 View (5)
18 Stress (6)
20 Moaned (6)
24 Cede (5)
26 Iron (5)
28 Memorise (5)
30 Moose (3)
32 Harbour (6)
33 Commenda-tion (6)
34 Adhesive (4)
35 Pinch (3)
36 Shout (4)

DOWN

2 Furnish (5)
3 Etch (7)
4 Ooze (4)
5 Beseech (4)
6 Taut (5)
7 Raise (7)
11 Decay (3)
12 Spring (3)
13 Family (3)
16 Pig-pen (3)
17 Wonderment (3)
19 Abbreviate (7)
21 Everyone (3)
22 Perfectly (7)
23 Fellow (3)
25 Sick (3)
27 Polish (5)
29 Royal (5)
30 Deserve (4)
31 Retain (4)

Evening Standard

89

ACROSS

1 Appeared (6)
5 Maintain (6)
8 Agreement (8)
9 Repast (4)
10 Meadow (3)
12 Roost (5)
15 Employ (3)
17 Ocean (3)
18 Tavern (3)
19 Aye (3)
20 Donated (5)
21 Devil (3)
22 Epoch (3)
23 Obtain (3)
24 Illuminated (3)
26 Elbow (5)
29 Fish (3)
33 Island (4)
34 Cosmos (8)
35 Fuel (6)
36 Simpler (6)

DOWN

2 Arouse (5)
3 Dumb (4)
4 Curtain (5)
5 Garret (5)
6 Hobble (4)
7 Tumbler (5)
10 True (5)
11 Advantage (5)
12 Heathen (5)
13 Wandered (5)
14 Turning-point (5)
15 Combine (5)
16 Eject (5)
25 Outcome (5)
27 Normal (5)
28 Filth (5)
30 Follow (5)
31 Dread (4)
32 Muddle (4)

90

ACROSS

1 Fissure (4)
4 Cur (3)
6 Bucket (4)
9 Edge (3)
10 Fall down (8)
11 Spoken (4)
14 Deed (3)
16 Drain (5)
19 Coined (8)
21 Singer (5)
23 Claimed (8)
24 Upright (5)
27 Gratuity (3)
31 Discourteous (4)
33 Idle (8)
34 Observe (3)
35 Repair (4)
36 Equipment (3)
37 Additional (4)

DOWN

2 Press (4)
3 Lofty (4)
4 Portrayed (8)
5 Increased (4)
6 Inclined (5)
7 Tune (3)
8 Likeness (5)
12 Name (5)
13 Elude (5)
14 Insect (3)
15 Principle (5)
17 Breezy (5)
18 Prompt (5)
20 Prevailing (8)
22 Knock (3)
25 Excite (5)
26 Belief (5)
28 Subside (4)
29 Staunch (4)
30 Finished (4)
32 Lair (3)

Evening Standard

91

ACROSS

4 Beg (5)
7 Habit (6)
9 Untruth (3)
10 Enclosure (3)
12 Offensive (5)
13 Discharge (4)
15 Not ever (5)

17 Haven (6)
19 Observe (4)
20 View (5)
22 Guided (3)
24 Wished (7)
27 Loiter (3)
28 Destined (5)
31 Flag (4)
33 Mild (6)

35 Wading-bird (5)
37 Deserve (4)
38 Boat (5)
39 Faucet (3)
41 Beam (3)
42 Soften (6)
43 Flat (5)

DOWN

1 Entry (6)
2 Hope (6)
3 Summit (3)
4 Long (4)
5 Memorise (5)
6 Height (8)
8 Food-list (4)

11 Careless (9)
14 Nurse (4)
16 Swerve (4)
18 Sense (4)
21 Bearing (8)
23 Adroit (4)
25 Story (4)
26 Valley (4)
29 Tormented (6)

30 Signify (6)
32 Twenty (5)
34 Close (4)
36 Genuine (4)
40 Favourite (3)

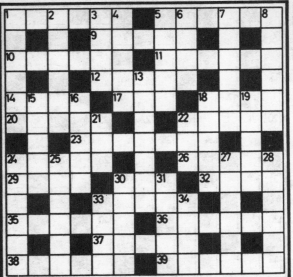

92

ACROSS

1 Austerity (6)
5 Purchased (6)
9 Rescuer (5)
10 Floor-covering (6)
11 Fish (6)
12 Spree (5)
14 Rush (4)
17 Spot (3)
18 Inlet (4)
20 Old-fashioned (5)
22 Heaped (5)
23 Nicked (7)
24 Rent (5)
26 Repulse (5)
29 Margin (4)
30 Encountered (3)
32 Discourteous (4)
33 Managed (5)
35 Appeared (6)
36 Race (6)
37 Change (5)
38 Nakedness (6)
39 Tie up (6)

DOWN

1 Disc (6)
2 Gem (6)
3 Employer (4)
4 Assessed (5)
5 Beleaguer (5)
6 Spoken (4)
7 Frolic (6)
8 Coloured (6)
13 Docket (7)
15 Relaxed (5)
16 Thick (5)
18 Drink (5)
19 Irritated (5)
21 Rabbit (3)
22 Through (3)
24 Diminish (6)
25 Concurred (6)
27 Discipline (6)
28 Thinner (6)
30 Furiously (5)
31 Principle (5)
33 Achievement (4)
34 Venture (4)

Evening Standard ═══

93

ACROSS

3 Capture (5)
9 Fish (6)
10 Noble (6)
11 Wrap (5)
12 Fashion (4)
15 Expense (4)
17 Gift (7)

DOWN

1 Stub (5)
2 Rank (5)
3 Lettuce (3)
4 Be there (6)
5 Still (4)
6 Colour (3)
7 Prestige (5)

20 Observe (3)
21 Plunged (5)
23 Level (4)
25 Direction (4)
26 Long (5)
28 Expert (3)
30 Air-spray (7)
33 Nearest (4)
35 Shade (4)

8 Condition (5)
13 Aperture (7)
14 Composition (5)
16 Portion (7)
18 Head-dress (5)
19 Stitch (3)
22 Storehouse (5)
24 Beverage (3)

36 Decoration (5)
38 Clergyman (6)
39 Pulling (6)
40 Cap (5)

27 Deny (6)
28 Irate (5)
29 Precise (5)
31 Compact (5)
32 Shelf (5)
34 Lake (4)
36 Crowd (3)
37 Fate (3)

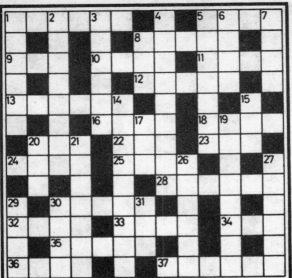

94

ACROSS

1 Scatter (6)
5 Dash (4)
8 Subsequently (5)
9 Odd (3)
10 Sign (4)
11 Hobble (4)
12 Performed (5)
13 Chaff (6)
16 Trade (4)
18 Revise (4)
20 Concealed (3)
22 Sick (3)
23 Fellow (3)
24 Pleasant (4)
25 Require (4)
28 Discuss (6)
30 Lesser (5)
32 Related (4)
33 Ascended (4)
34 Devil (3)
35 Respond (5)
36 Regretted (4)
37 Posture (6)

DOWN

1 Writer (6)
2 Amorous (8)
3 Worshipped (6)
4 Annulled (9)
5 Erased (7)
6 Parched (4)
7 Sort (4)
8 Meadow (3)
14 Strengthen (9)
15 Can (3)
17 Beer (3)
19 Gift (8)
20 Strike (3)
21 Delineated (7)
26 Beat (6)
27 Folk (6)
29 Couple (4)
30 Mud (4)
31 Decay (3)

Evening Standard ═══════

ACROSS

1 Slumbered (5)
5 Imitated (6)
8 Deposit (5)
10 Venerate (6)
11 Deceased (4)
14 Encipher (6)
15 Photograph (7)
18 Lair (3)
19 Spike (3)
21 Act (4)
23 Flower (5)
24 Unite (4)
27 Fixed (3)
29 Scull (3)
31 Fussed (7)
32 Refrain (6)
34 Joint (4)
35 Worn (6)
38 Senior (5)
39 Totter (6)
40 Dissuade (5)

DOWN

2 Shelter (3)
3 Ample (6)
4 Hill (3)
5 Yield (4)
6 Situated (6)
7 Rely (6)
9 Dishearten (7)
12 Stop (3)
13 Finished (4)
16 Inactive (4)
17 Consumed (5)
20 Withdrew (7)
22 Sea-eagle (4)
24 Evil (6)
25 Appearance (4)
26 Mended (6)
28 Disregard (6)
30 Regret (3)
33 Prophet (4)
36 Colour (3)
37 Stretch (3)

96

ACROSS

2 Elbow (5)
7 Island (4)
8 Victor (6)
9 Jam (5)
11 Help (3)
13 Spoil (3)
15 Sketched (4)

DOWN

1 Moving (5)
2 Novel (3)
3 Father (3)
4 Sheep (3)
5 Tavern (3)
6 Prevent (5)
10 Objective (4)

16 Club (3)
18 Present (4)
19 Postponed (7)
20 Discharge (4)
22 Sapient (4)
23 Edited (7)
25 Paradise (4)
27 Bow (3)
28 Naked (4)

11 Stuck (7)
12 Wished (7)
13 Of medicine (7)
14 Venerated (7)
16 Start (5)
17 Domesticated (5)
18 Chop (3)

30 Defective (3)
31 Youth (3)
33 Condition (5)
36 Operative (6)
37 Placed (4)
38 Ruin (5)

21 Number (3)
24 Kind (4)
26 Dullard (5)
29 Swift (5)
32 Intelligence (3)
33 Stitch (3)
34 Wonder (3)
35 Moose (3)

Evening Standard

ACROSS

2 Indolence (5)
7 Cite (5)
8 Decoration (5)
10 Alternative (5)
12 Transgress (3)
13 Begin (5)
15 Determined (7)

17 Called (6)
19 Turf (3)
20 Denied (7)
23 Require (4)
25 Bowl (4)
26 Deciphered (7)
30 Feline (3)
31 Discussion (6)
34 Collected (7)

37 Renovate (5)
38 Attempt (3)
39 Demon (5)
40 Cap (5)
41 Giver (5)
42 Scatter (5)

DOWN

1 Absolutely (5)
2 Rage (5)
3 Epistle (6)
4 Fastened (4)
5 Lived (7)
6 Declined (5)
9 Performed (3)

11 Continued (7)
13 Stench (5)
14 Equipped (5)
16 Bed (3)
18 Signified (7)
21 Couch (5)
22 Hurled (5)
24 Rotten (7)
27 Tin (3)

28 Scorn (6)
29 Change (5)
32 Underneath (5)
33 Singer (5)
35 Stray (3)
36 Adroit (4)

98

ACROSS

1 Suspended (4)
4 Seed (3)
6 Spoken (4)
8 Amuse (6)
9 Confused (6)
10 Fowl (3)
12 Started (5)
14 Ordeal (5)
15 Outcoming (5)
18 Erase (6)
20 Revised (6)
24 Sewer (5)
26 Scanty (5)
28 Adhesive (5)
30 Guided (3)
32 Spite (6)
33 Beast (6)
34 Formerly (4)
35 Pinch (3)
36 Pull (4)

DOWN

2 Combine (5)
3 Hand-bomb (7)
4 Track (4)
5 Scheme (4)
6 Command (5)
7 Mean (7)
11 Bird (3)
12 Wicked (3)
13 Entrap (3)
16 Cot (3)
17 Beverage (3)
19 Elucidate (7)
21 Immerse (3)
22 Silliness (7)
23 Expire (3)
25 Fish-eggs (3)
27 Elevate (5)
29 Coach (5)
30 Thin (4)
31 Moist (4)

Evening Standard

99

ACROSS

1 Enquiring (6)
5 Agreement (6)
8 Decided (8)
9 Obstinate (4)
10 Spring (3)
12 Tender (5)
15 Pig-pen (3)
17 Animal (3)
18 Astern (3)
19 Epoch (3)
20 Characteristic (5)
21 Imitate (3)
22 Wrath (3)
23 Fish (3)
24 Males (3)
26 Reigned (5)
29 Cover (3)
33 Fair (4)
34 Solitary (8)
35 Actor (6)
36 Skilful (6)

DOWN

2 Precipitous (5)
3 Flag (4)
4 Sorrow (5)
5 Subject (5)
6 Whirlpool (4)
7 Confidence (5)
10 Vapour (5)
11 Anew (5)
12 Exterior (5)
13 Feeble (5)
14 Assessed (5)
15 Booth (5)
16 Cede (5)
25 Equivalent (5)
27 Below (5)
28 Follow (5)
30 Bury (5)
31 Remain (4)
32 Smack (4)

100

ACROSS

1 Cease (4)
4 Cur (3)
6 Caution (4)
9 Expert (3)
10 Horrible (8)
11 Knife (4)
14 Heap (3)

16 Trivial (5)
19 Idol-
  worshipper (8)
21 Allude (5)
23 Degenerate (8)
24 Waterway (5)
27 Rank (3)
31 Snatch (4)
33 Shortened (8)

34 Sick (3)
35 Inactive (4)
36 Golf-peg (3)
37 Comfort (4)

DOWN

2 Rotate (4)
3 Act (4)
4 Beaten (8)
5 Swallow (4)
6 Squander (5)
7 Deed (3)
8 Respond (5)

12 Municipal (5)
13 Twelve (5)
14 Fighting (3)
15 Postpone (5)
17 Soar (5)
18 Youngster (5)
20 Resort (8)
22 Uncooked (3)
25 Pungent (5)

26 Stroll (5)
28 Wagon (4)
29 Rim (4)
30 Muddle (4)
32 Every (3)

Evening Standard

101

ACROSS

4 Rescued (5)
7 Regard (6)
9 Damp (3)
10 Favourite (3)
12 Choose (5)
13 Excursion (4)
15 Stadium (5)

DOWN

1 Grant (6)
2 Dress (6)
3 Vitality (3)
4 Observed (4)
5 Map-book (5)
6 Intrude (8)
8 Food (4)

17 Reposed (6)
19 Anon (4)
20 Pup (5)
22 Object (3)
24 Worried (7)
27 Vegetable (3)
28 Darkness (5)
31 Prima donna (4)

11 Handling (9)
14 Wealth (4)
16 Revise (4)
18 Nimble (4)
21 Wavering (8)
23 Repair (4)
25 Comfort (4)
26 Expired (4)
29 Soiled (6)

33 Remitter (6)
35 View (5)
37 Nobleman (4)
38 Lariat (5)
39 Faucet (3)
41 Epoch (3)
42 Fall (6)
43 Condition (5)

30 Poured (6)
32 Advantage (5)
34 Tidy (4)
36 Centre (4)
40 Placed (3)

102

ACROSS

1 Harsh (6)
5 Clergyman (6)
9 Bird (5)
10 Vibrate (6)
11 View (6)
12 Liability (5)
14 Bogus (4)
17 Lair (3)
18 Leer (4)
20 Candle (5)
22 Liberated (5)
23 Passed on (7)
24 Lukewarm (5)
26 Courage (5)
29 Discharge (4)
30 Serpent (3)
32 Rush (4)
33 Slumber (5)
35 Item (6)
36 Voucher (6)
37 Sum (5)
38 Sweet (6)
39 Guide (6)

DOWN

1 Unfair (6)
2 Abduct (6)
3 Require (4)
4 Ventured (5)
5 Simple (5)
6 Repose (4)
7 Appear (6)
8 Added (6)
13 For (7)
15 Seraglio (5)
16 Deserve (5)
18 Command (5)
19 Depart (5)
21 Colour (3)
22 Marshland (3)
24 Nursed (6)
25 Hand-gun (6)
27 Smelled (6)
28 Reviser (6)
30 Apportion (5)
31 Flower Part (5)
33 Location (4)
34 Heap (4)

Evening Standard

103

ACROSS

3 Begin (5)
9 Ass (6)
10 Simpler (6)
11 Coach (5)
12 Heroic (4)
15 Denomination (4)
17 Relate (7)
20 Sorrow (3)
21 High building (5)
23 Just (4)
25 Pool (4)
26 Hut (5)
28 Expert (3)
30 Stopping (7)
33 Agitate (4)
35 Pedigree (4)
36 Artery (5)
38 Free (6)
39 Refuse (6)
40 Keen (5)

DOWN

1 Viper (5)
2 Caper (5)
3 Fixed (3)
4 Despot (6)
5 Control (4)
6 Brown (3)
7 Tendon (5)
8 Banal (5)
13 Faultless (7)
14 Funny (5)
16 Forgive (7)
18 Pick-me-up (5)
19 Material (3)
22 Perch (5)
24 Butt (3)
27 Snuggle (6)
28 Enquired (5)
29 Sea-duck (5)
31 Angry (5)
32 Kind (5)
34 Roster (4)
36 Imitate (3)
37 Tune (3)

104

ACROSS

1 Haunt (6)
5 Righteous (4)
8 Long (5)
9 Observe (3)
10 Mirth (4)
11 Skin-trouble (4)
12 Fish (5)
13 Evoke (6)
16 Title (4)
18 Deadened (4)
20 For each (3)
22 Sleep (3)
23 Animal (3)
24 Air (4)
25 Journey (4)
28 Soften (6)
30 Traded (5)
32 Temper (4)
33 Press (4)
34 Child (3)
35 Untidy (5)
36 Fastened (4)
37 Dive (6)

DOWN

1 Ventured (6)
2 Sample (8)
3 Recover (6)
4 Apiarist (9)
5 Grille (7)
6 Formerly (4)
7 Consider (4)
8 Aye (3)
14 Tease (9)
15 Bird (3)
17 Spoil (3)
19 Undefeated (8)
20 Young Dog (3)
21 Ebbed (7)
26 Dog-house (6)
27 Figure (6)
29 Exclude (4)
30 Cupola (4)
31 Attempt (3)

Evening Standard

105

ACROSS

1 Guide (5)
5 Dastard (6)
8 Regional (5)
10 Vegetable (6)
11 Greedy (4)
14 Part (6)
15 Favour (7)
18 Males (3)
19 Finish (3)
21 Adroit (4)
23 Bury (5)
24 Aperture (4)
27 Number (3)
29 Can (3)
31 Turned (7)
32 Swerved (6)
34 Companion (4)
35 Pass (6)
38 Helped (5)
39 Stretch (6)
40 Principle (5)

DOWN

2 Also (3)
3 Exhilarated (6)
4 Decay (3)
5 Clothed (4)
6 Relinquished (6)
7 Proper (6)
9 Satisfied (7)
12 Vigour (3)
13 Eat (4)
16 Egg-shaped (4)
17 Go in (5)
20 Signified (7)
22 Repute (4)
24 Strict (6)
25 Detail (4)
26 Diatribe (6)
28 Display (6)
30 Entrap (3)
33 Deceased (4)
36 Permit (3)
37 Prosecute (3)

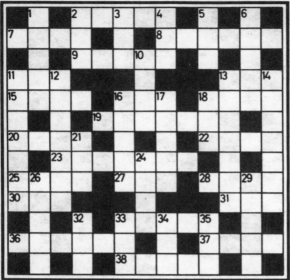

106

ACROSS

2 Concerning (5)
7 Clothed (4)
8 Save (6)
9 Thick (5)
11 Marry (3)
13 Fish (3)
15 Candid (4)

DOWN

1 Slumber (5)
2 Append (3)
3 Possess (3)
4 Golf-peg (3)
5 Expert (3)
6 Ghost (5)
10 Anon (4)

16 Hill (3)
18 Garden tool (4)
19 Widespread (7)
20 Spoke (4)
22 Mirth (4)
23 Fundamental (7)
25 Detail (4)

11 Adore (7)
12 Wished (7)
13 Unfeeling (7)
14 Erased (7)
16 Lukewarm (5)
17 Pass on (5)
18 Tease (3)
21 Barrier (3)
24 Visit (4)

27 Age (3)
28 Rage (4)
30 Cushion (3)
31 Mournful (3)
33 Demand (5)
36 Picture-house (6)
37 Revise (4)
38 Staff (5)

26 Implicit (5)
29 Madness (5)
32 Novel (3)
33 Taxi (3)
34 Deed (3)
35 Males (3)

Evening Standard

107

ACROSS

2 Composition (5)
7 Suspect (5)
8 Acute (5)
10 Fundamental (5)
12 Finish (3)

DOWN

1 Paper size (5)
2 Receded (5)
3 Gaped (6)
4 Greedy (4)
5 Playhouse (7)
6 Command (5)
9 Insect (3)

13 Sea-duck (5)
15 Gave (7)
17 Laden (6)
19 Entrap (3)
20 Sweet (7)
23 Fastened (4)
25 Comfort (4)
26 Challenging (7)

11 Agree (7)
13 Chosen (5)
14 Stupefied (5)
16 Born (3)
18 Scorned (7)
21 Accepted (5)
22 Trivial (5)
24 Determined (7)

30 Rotter (3)
31 Gift (6)
34 Expected (7)
37 Cash (5)
38 Help (3)
39 Squat (5)
40 Heaped (5)
41 Keen (5)
42 Gem (5)

27 Obese (3)
28 Interfere (6)
29 Lover (5)
32 True (5)
33 Not ever (5)
35 Sicken (3)
36 Cheat (4)

108

ACROSS

1 Droop (4)
4 Seed (3)
6 Rescue (4)
8 Disfigure (6)
9 Fold (6)
10 Fitting (3)
12 Near (5)

DOWN

2 Perfect (5)
3 Passage (7)
4 Excuse (4)
5 Treaty (4)
6 Absolute (5)
7 Trace (7)
11 Mine (3)

14 Sewer (5)
15 Angry (5)
18 Instrument (6)
20 Worshipped (6)
24 Engine (5)
26 Passionate (5)
28 Dizzy (5)
30 Favourite (3)

12 Tooth (3)
13 Epoch (3)
16 Limb (3)
17 Consume (3)
19 Regular (7)
21 Cur (3)
22 Aperture (7)
23 Parched (3)
25 Poem (3)

32 Numbness (6)
33 Evoke (6)
34 Sign (4)
35 Obscure (3)
36 Margin (4)

27 Mature (5)
29 Performing (5)
30 Poke (4)
31 Side (4)

Evening Standard

109

ACROSS

1 Felt (6)
5 Scatter (6)
8 Recommend (8)
9 Staunch (4)
10 Lettuce (3)
12 Booth (5)
15 Feline animal (3)
17 Circuit (3)
18 Sick (3)
19 Fuss (3)
20 Open (5)
21 Sphere (3)
22 Equality (3)
23 Headgear (3)
24 Fasten (3)
26 Name (5)
29 Colour (3)
33 Retain (4)
34 Wave (8)
35 Figurine (6)
36 Agreement (6)

DOWN

2 Wireless (5)
3 Plan (4)
4 Traded (5)
5 Odour (5)
6 Danger (4)
7 Stadium (5)
10 Vessel (5)
11 Incline (5)
12 Fun (5)
13 Deflect (5)
14 Supple (5)
15 Material (5)
16 List (5)
25 Unsuitable (5)
27 Steep (5)
28 Smallest (5)
30 Overturn (5)
31 Dot (4)
32 Inactive (4)

110

ACROSS

1 Inform (4)
4 Line (3)
6 Destiny (4)
9 Sheep (3)
10 Find (8)
11 Marquee (4)
14 Lever (3)
16 Worship (5)
19 Intricate (8)
21 Postpone (5)
23 Representative (8)
24 Scope (5)
27 Tear (3)
31 Larger amount (4)
33 Idle (8)
34 Owing (3)
35 Observed (4)
36 Expire (3)
37 Saucy (4)

DOWN

2 Discharge (4)
3 Shortage (4)
4 Disclosed (8)
5 Twist (4)
6 Foul (5)
7 Wonder (3)
8 Singer (5)
12 Viper (5)
13 Blemish (5)
14 Offer (3)
15 Allude (5)
17 Harmonium (5)
18 Surpass (5)
20 Dainty (8)
22 Material (3)
25 Dwelling (5)
26 Verdant (5)
28 Object (4)
29 Cease (4)
30 Declare (4)
32 Regret (3)

111

ACROSS

4 Scholar (5)
7 Maintain (6)
9 Enthusiast (3)
10 Mineral (3)
12 Firearm (5)
13 Flower (4)
15 Attack (5)

DOWN

1 Madman (6)
2 Fish (6)
3 Self (3)
4 Trim (4)
5 Combine (5)
6 Inactivity (8)
8 Cupid (4)

17 Pure (6)
19 Sea-eagle (4)
20 Crawl (5)
22 Knock (3)
24 Discussed (7)
27 Lair (3)
28 Delete (5)
31 Jetty (4)
33 Climbed (6)

11 Enchanted (9)
14 Hut (4)
16 Chair (4)
18 Imitated (4)
21 Roll (8)
23 Rind (4)
25 Elite (4)
26 Sketched (4)

35 Following (5)
37 Timber (4)
38 Condition (5)
39 Immerse (3)
41 Sick (3)
42 Debase (6)
43 Dribble (5)

29 Worshipped (6)
30 Finish (6)
32 Proportion (5)
34 Parched (4)
36 Dropped (4)
40 Favourite (3)

112

ACROSS

1 Crease (6)

5 Turmoil (6)

9 Silly (5)

10 Jammed (6)

11 Server (6)

12 Less (5)

14 Thoroughfare (4)

17 Performed (3)

18 Blaze (4)

20 Ate (5)

22 Apportion (5)

23 Slavery (7)

24 Send (5)

26 Weird (5)

29 Revise (4)

30 Insect (3)

32 Tunny (4)

33 Animal (5)

35 Term (6)

36 Tidy (6)

37 Abrupt (5)

38 Dashed (6)

39 Evaded (6)

DOWN

1 Recompense (6)

2 Maniac (6)

3 Gladly (4)

4 Finished (5)

5 Unmarried (5)

6 Close (4)

7 Necessitate (6)

8 Objective (6)

13 Meandering (7)

15 Lubricated (5)

16 Liability (5)

18 Swift (5)

19 Bird (5)

21 Spot (3)

22 Era (3)

24 Harvested (6)

25 Reflect (6)

27 Corroded (6)

28 Deserved (6)

30 Helped (5)

31 Taut (5)

33 Carry (4)

34 Stagger (4)

Evening Standard

113

ACROSS

3 Twenty (5)
9 Wave (6)
10 Exertion (6)
11 Principle (5)
12 Muddle (4)
15 Lake (4)
17 Perform (7)
20 Material (3)
21 Burst (5)
23 Employed (4)
25 Air (4)
26 Irrigate (5)
28 Ate (3)
30 Dedicated (7)
33 Thought (4)
35 Travel (4)
36 Annoyance (5)
38 Floating (6)
39 Cycle (6)
40 Flat (5)

DOWN

1 Filth (5)
2 Shut (5)
3 Fixed (3)
4 Make (6)
5 Rush (4)
6 Newt (3)
7 Cringe (5)
8 Precipitous (5)
13 Pardoned (7)
14 Twist (5)
16 Ebbed (7)
18 Made a mistake (5)
19 Fitting (3)
22 Teacher (5)
24 Barrier (3)
27 Decline (6)
28 Last (5)
29 Traded (5)
31 Shy (5)
32 Thick (5)
34 Location (4)
36 Friend (3)
37 Fish (3)

114

ACROSS

1 Hinder (6)
5 Bogus (4)
8 Express (5)
9 Transgress (3)
10 Conceited (4)
11 Speed (4)
12 Advantage (5)

DOWN

1 Interior (6)
2 Sorry (8)
3 Pious (6)
4 Agreed (9)
5 Twisted (7)
6 Warmth (4)
7 Encounter (4)

13 Deviation (6)
16 Sea-bird (4)
18 Cheese (4)
20 Finish (3)
22 Healthy (3)
23 Cur (3)
24 Destiny (4)
25 Paradise (4)
28 Plan (6)

8 By way of (3)
14 Allusion (9)
15 Loiter (3)
17 Free (3)
19 Home (8)
20 Consume (3)
21 Erased (7)
26 Snuggle (6)
27 Purpose (6)

30 Spree (5)
32 Defeat (4)
33 Tidy (4)
34 Wrath (3)
35 Respond (5)
36 Watched (4)
37 Modern (6)

29 Competent (4)
30 Unusual (4)
31 Permit (3)

Evening Standard ===

115

ACROSS

1 Upright (5)
5 Weak (6)
8 Hurry (5)
10 Account (6)
11 Discharge (4)
14 Hidden (6)
15 Idea (7)

18 Vegetable (3)
19 Cushion (3)
21 Cart (4)
23 Under (5)
24 Aperture (4)
27 Fellow (3)
29 Hog (3)
31 Unaffected (7)
32 Swerved (6)

34 Title (4)
35 Worn (6)
38 Viper (5)
39 Stretch (6)
40 Object (5)

DOWN

2 Regret (3)
3 Option (6)
4 Sailor (3)
5 Sense (4)
6 Departed (6)
7 Coarse (6)
9 Ceased (7)

12 Chart (3)
13 Rip (4)
16 Spoken (4)
17 Claw (5)
20 Given (7)
22 Region (4)
24 Strict (6)
25 Candid (4)
26 Diatribe (6)

28 Rage (6)
30 Jewel (3)
33 Deceased (4)
36 Colour (3)
37 Bird (3)

116

ACROSS

2 Correct (5)
7 Cupid (4)
8 Discharge (6)
9 Form (5)
11 Mournful (3)
13 Regret (3)
15 Paradise (4)
16 Vegetable (3)
18 Consider (4)
19 Severe (7)
20 Implement (4)
22 Otherwise (4)
23 Cut (7)
25 Revise (4)
27 Noise (3)
28 Unfasten (4)
30 Groove (3)
31 Stray (3)
33 Started (5)
36 Operative (6)
37 One (4)
38 Storehouse (5)

DOWN

1 Wide (5)
2 Donkey (3)
3 Epoch (3)
4 Owing (3)
5 Artful (3)
6 Obscure (5)
10 Excuse (4)
11 Colonist (7)
12 Lodge (7)
13 Rest (7)
14 Monarch (7)
16 Snooped (5)
17 Pale (5)
18 Expire (3)
21 Permit (3)
24 Ascend (4)
26 Dullard (5)
29 Sewer (5)
32 Pinch (3)
33 Cot (3)
34 Breach (3)
35 Fruit (3)

Evening Standard

117

ACROSS

2 Dawdle (5)
7 Hell (5)
8 Enquired (5)
10 Mix (5)
12 Strike (3)
13 Outcome (5)
15 Gave (7)

17 Sofa (6)
19 Barrier (3)
20 Promised (7)
23 Cheese (4)
25 Sketch (4)
26 Strife (7)
30 Entrap (3)
31 Shouted (6)
34 Expected (7)

37 Untrue (5)
38 Tree (3)
39 Liability (5)
40 Worth (5)
41 Lawful (5)
42 Command (5)

DOWN

1 Elevate (5)
2 Outcoming (5)
3 Slumbering (6)
4 Disembark (4)
5 Abashed (7)
6 Dissuade (5)
9 Equipment (3)

11 Tottery (7)
13 Island (5)
14 Place (5)
16 Horse (3)
18 Voted (7)
21 Exercise (5)
22 Vegetable (5)
24 Least (7)
27 Fixed (3)

28 Pollute (6)
29 Curse (5)
32 Subsequently (5)
33 Composition (5)
35 Everything (3)
36 Expensive (4)

118

ACROSS

1 Roster (4)
4 Firearm (3)
6 Oaf (4)
8 Pure (6)
9 Counsel (6)
10 Consume (3)
12 Fragrance (5)

14 Serious (5)
15 Arouse (5)
18 Killing (6)
20 Character (6)
24 Emblem (5)
26 Robust (5)
28 Bird (5)
30 Favourite (3)
32 Legal (6)

33 Stick (6)
34 Ale (4)
35 Fasten (3)
36 Regretted (4)

DOWN

2 Alternative (5)
3 Supposed (7)
4 Mirth (4)
5 Tidy (4)
6 Paramour (5)
7 Expose (7)
11 Enquire (3)

12 Purpose (3)
13 Greeting (3)
16 Sphere (3)
17 Finish (3)
19 Ignorant (7)
21 Era (3)
22 Tutor (7)
23 Stretch (3)
25 Expert (3)

27 Postpone (5)
29 Big (5)
30 Plan (4)
31 Domesticated (4)

119

ACROSS

1 Objective (6)
5 Strict (6)
8 Meet (8)
9 Vanquish (4)
10 Network (3)
12 Applaud (5)
15 Lair (3)
17 Scull (3)
18 Tune (3)
19 Beverage (3)
20 Foreigner (5)
21 Sea-bird (3)
22 Uncooked (3)
23 Jewel (3)
24 Free (3)
26 Supple (5)
29 Plus (3)
33 Detail (4)
34 Forbearance (8)
35 Cruel (6)
36 Tremble (6)

DOWN

2 Worship (5)
3 Grant (4)
4 Flashlight (5)
5 View (5)
6 Change (4)
7 Awaken (5)
10 Irrigate (5)
11 Plank (5)
12 Creep (5)
13 Eject (5)
14 Scope (5)
15 Play (5)
16 Nude (5)
25 Bury (5)
27 Drive (5)
28 Loathed (5)
30 Recess (5)
31 Discharge (4)
32 Plague (4)

120

ACROSS

1 Gasp (4)
4 Total (3)
6 Pace (4)
9 Hill (3)
10 Representative (8)
11 Peak (4)

14 Wonder (3)
16 Harmony (5)
19 Heath (8)
21 Strayed (5)
23 Sled (8)
24 Pool (5)
27 Record (3)
31 Scoff (4)
33 Tester (8)

34 Always (3)
35 Ran (4)
36 Equality (3)
37 Dummy (4)

DOWN

2 Imitated (4)
3 Pour (4)
4 Sturdy (8)
5 Encounter (4)
6 Blemish (5)
7 Summit (3)
8 Upright (5)

12 Slap (5)
13 Brag (5)
14 Beer (3)
15 Enlist (5)
17 Likeness (5)
18 Youthful (5)
20 Suave (8)
22 Cur (3)
25 Perfect (5)

26 Weary (5)
28 Retain (4)
29 Locate (4)
30 Shout (4)
32 Watch (3)

Evening Standard

121

ACROSS

4 Clutch (5)
7 Free (6)
9 Sorrow (3)
10 Wand (3)
12 Deflect (5)
13 Pitcher (4)
15 Material (5)

DOWN

1 Concurred (6)
2 Cave (6)
3 Conifer (3)
4 Objective (4)
5 Spree (5)
6 Shrivelled (8)

17 Rest (6)
19 Thoroughfare (4)
20 Eater (5)
22 Feline animal (3)
24 Given (7)
27 For each (3)
28 Stadium (5)

8 Unaccompanied (4)
11 Rejected (9)
14 Rush (4)
16 Chair (4)
18 Support (4)
21 Point out (8)
23 Rip (4)
25 Tidy (4)

31 Overlook (4)
33 Worshipped (6)
35 Irrigate (5)
37 Desire (4)
38 Seraglio (5)
39 Barrier (3)
41 Help (3)
42 Lounged (6)
43 Was told (5)

26 Sketched (4)
29 Eatable (6)
30 Refer (6)
32 Curse (5)
34 Spoken (4)
36 Between (4)
40 Crowd (3)

122

ACROSS

1 Niche (6)
5 Impede (6)
9 Sea (5)
10 Column (6)
11 Bulk (6)
12 Bird (5)
14 Bogus (4)

17 Enclosure (3)
18 Present (4)
20 Weary (5)
22 Died away (5)
23 Withdrew (7)
24 Lac (5)
26 Outcoming (5)
29 Revise (4)
30 Bribe (3)

32 Tender (4)
33 Declined (5)
35 Item (6)
36 Firewood (6)
37 Opposite (5)
38 Blush (6)
39 Guide (6)

DOWN

1 Meal (6)
2 Vault (6)
3 Fly (4)
4 Fragment (5)
5 Harbour (5)
6 Soon (4)
7 Hesitated (6)

8 Staggered (6)
13 Meat (7)
15 Leased (5)
16 Deserve (5)
18 Hell (5)
19 Happen again (5)
21 Lair (3)
22 Dined (3)

24 Give (6)
25 Filtered (6)
27 United (6)
28 Dread (6)
30 Gallery (5)
31 Leaf (5)
33 Dry (4)
34 Dreadful (4)

Evening Standard

123

ACROSS

3 Concerning (5)
9 Display (6)
10 Squalid (6)
11 Alternative (5)
12 Too (4)
15 Face (4)
17 Lived (7)
20 Attempt (3)
21 Royal (5)
23 Observed (4)
25 Roster (4)
26 Couch (5)
28 Curve (3)
30 Retribution (7)
33 Defeated (4)
35 Regretted (4)
36 Tooth (5)
38 Beetle (6)
39 Web (6)
40 Played (5)

DOWN

1 Javelin (5)
2 Coarse (5)
3 Fuss (3)
4 Improve (6)
5 Employed (4)
6 Hill (3)
7 Confess (5)
8 Strangely (5)
13 Ease (7)
14 Lubricated (5)
16 Dispose (7)
18 Prevent (5)
19 Equality (3)
22 Paramour (5)
24 Nothing (3)
27 Deny (6)
28 Demean (5)
29 Waterway (5)
31 Tender (5)
32 Bordered (5)
34 Tramp (4)
36 Rug (3)
37 Free (3)

124

ACROSS

1 Save (6)
5 Imitated (4)
8 Feel (5)
9 Tin (3)
10 Dregs (4)
11 Bow (4)
12 Advantage (5)

13 Laboured (6)
16 Sea-bird (4)
18 Staunch (4)
20 Owing (3)
22 Record (3)
23 Epoch (3)
24 Bearing (4)
25 Detail (4)
28 Devastate (6)

30 Taut (5)
32 Encounter (4)
33 Ripped (4)
34 Vase (3)
35 Slumber (5)
36 Entrance (4)
37 Avaricious (6)

DOWN

1 Rouse (6)
2 Go on (8)
3 Chicken (6)
4 Courier (9)
5 Slander (7)
6 Saucy (4)
7 Daybreak (4)

8 Ocean (3)
14 Charmed (9)
15 Beverage (3)
17 Decay (3)
19 Riches (8)
20 Obscure (3)
21 Name (7)
26 Method (6)
27 Eagerly (6)

29 Self-satisfied (4)
30 Trial (4)
31 Summit (3)

Evening Standard

125

ACROSS

1 Slumbered (5)
5 Instructed (6)
8 Dangerous (5)
10 Thoroughfare (6)
11 Staff (4)
14 Worn (6)
15 Try (7)
18 Sack (3)
19 Cushion (3)
21 Expensive (4)
23 Storehouse (5)
24 Muddle (4)
27 Noise (3)
29 Circuit (3)
31 Fundamental (7)
32 Tremble (6)
34 Fruit (4)
35 Simply (6)
38 Elbow (5)
39 Soften (6)
40 Order (5)

DOWN

2 Fate (3)
3 Favour (6)
4 Fasten (3)
5 Kind (4)
6 Discharge (6)
7 Offer (6)
9 Ceased (7)
12 Sphere (3)
13 Border (4)
16 Story (4)
17 Animal (5)
20 Given (7)
22 Region (4)
24 Conquer (6)
25 Slipped (4)
26 Fierce (6)
28 Overlooked (6)
30 Favourite (3)
33 Torn (4)
36 Era (3)
37 Resin (3)

126

ACROSS

2 Inlet (5)
7 Fete (4)
8 Property (6)
9 Prompt (5)
11 Sick (3)
13 Performed (3)
15 Temper (4)
16 Prow (3)
18 Withered (4)
19 Maybe (7)
20 Rip (4)
22 Shout (4)
23 Shyly (7)
25 Fastened (4)
27 Pinch (3)
28 Above (4)
30 Finish (3)
31 Watch (3)
33 Haul (5)
36 Expel (6)
37 Attack (4)
38 Irrigate (5)

DOWN

1 Greeting (5)
2 Vehicle (3)
3 Epoch (3)
4 Lock-opener (3)
5 Consumed (3)
6 Step (5)
10 Entrance (4)
11 Copy (7)
12 Found (7)
13 Merit (7)
14 Aver (7)
16 Start (5)
17 Pup (5)
18 Agent (3)
21 Free (3)
24 Plunge (4)
26 Bury (5)
29 Nest (5)
32 Intimidate (3)
33 Chop (3)
34 Astern (3)
35 Go wrong (3)

Evening Standard

127

ACROSS

2 Bottle (5)
7 House (5)
8 Worship (5)
10 Seraph (5)
12 Help (3)
13 Sober (5)
15 Creased (7)
17 Pantry (6)
19 Feline animal (3)
20 Delineated (7)
23 Watched (4)
25 Adroit (4)
26 Obtained (7)
30 Mournful (3)
31 Relate (6)
34 Expected (7)
37 Old-fashioned (5)
38 Conifer (3)
39 Object (5)
40 Enticed (5)
41 Stop (5)
42 Avarice (5)

DOWN

1 View (5)
2 Tartan cloth (5)
3 Passed (6)
4 Declare (4)
5 Adjusted (7)
6 Command (5)
9 Lubricate (3)
11 Match (7)
13 Slumber (5)
14 Equipped (5)
16 Male (3)
18 Lived (7)
21 Liability (5)
22 War-horse (5)
24 Wished (7)
27 Rodent (3)
28 Infer (6)
29 Dreadful (5)
32 Bothered (5)
33 Taut (5)
35 Tune (3)
36 Expensive (4)

128

ACROSS

1 Elderly (4)
4 Cushion (3)
6 Enormous (4)
8 Smart (6)
9 Ripe (6)
10 Faucet (3)
12 Under (5)
14 Inexpensive (5)
15 Revolt (5)
18 Erase (6)
20 Exhilarated (6)
24 Vision (5)
26 Extra (5)
28 Adhesive (5)
30 Fitting (3)
32 Hue (6)
33 Evoke (6)
34 Skilful (4)
35 Defective (3)
36 Increased (4)

DOWN

2 Rank (5)
3 Lament (7)
4 Saucy (4)
5 Tip (4)
6 Obstacle (5)
7 Rubbish (7)
11 Beer (3)
12 Evil (3)
13 Damp (3)
16 Cot (3)
17 Shelter (3)
19 Burst (7)
21 Circuit (3)
22 Astounding (7)
23 Owing (3)
25 Tear (3)
27 Perch (5)
29 Banal (5)
30 Parched (4)
31 Nurse (4)

Evening Standard

129

ACROSS

1 Fight (6)
5 Shrewd (6)
8 Rule (8)
9 Top (4)
10 Network (3)
12 Royal (5)
15 Fix (3)

DOWN

2 Ascended (5)
3 Excursion (4)
4 Delete (5)
5 Stadium (5)
6 Snare (4)
7 Subject (5)
10 Tired (5)

17 Meadow (3)
18 Employ (3)
19 Hatchet (3)
20 Coach (5)
21 Fasten (3)
22 Prosecute (3)
23 Obtain (3)
24 Aye (3)
26 Evade (5)

11 Consecrate (5)
12 Assessed (5)
13 Splendid (5)
14 Thrust (5)
15 Trivial (5)
16 Verdant (5)
25 Happening (5)
27 Proprietor (5)
28 Estimate (5)

29 Longing (3)
33 Opening (4)
34 Repulsive (8)
35 Coma (6)
36 Simply (6)

30 Equivalent (5)
31 Cease (4)
32 Minus (4)

130

ACROSS

1 Bridge (4)
4 Barrier (3)
6 Chop (4)
9 Sicken (3)
10 Dead (8)
11 Self-satisfied (4)

14 Dog (3)
16 Edge (5)
19 Advanced (8)
21 Postpone (5)
23 Disfigured (8)
24 Short (5)
27 Colour (3)
31 Trick (4)
33 Obsolete (8)

34 Lair (3)
35 Pip (4)
36 Insane (3)
37 Comfort (4)

DOWN

2 Nobleman (4)
3 Require (4)
4 Argued (8)
5 Manufactured (4)
6 Hurry (5)
7 Objective (3)

8 Held (5)
12 Fun (5)
13 Engine (5)
14 Fish (3)
15 Allude (5)
17 Spacious (5)
18 Dodge (5)
20 Beaten (8)
22 Wand (3)

25 Ooze (5)
26 Pass (5)
28 Fate (4)
29 Naked (4)
30 Muddle (4)
32 Observe (3)

Evening Standard

131

ACROSS

4 Wind (5)
7 Slumbering (6)
9 Strive (3)
10 Cot (3)
12 Lesser (5)
13 Cupid (4)
15 Jockey (5)

17 Conflict (6)
19 Expensive (4)
20 Unfasten (5)
22 Marshland (3)
24 Ebbed (7)
27 Because (3)
28 Upright (5)
31 Facts (4)
33 Repaired (6)

35 View (5)
37 Sapient (4)
38 Same (5)
39 Faucet (3)
41 Epoch (3)
42 Modern (6)
43 Learnt (5)

DOWN

1 Cake (6)
2 Nearly (6)
3 Network (3)
4 Season (4)
5 Eerie (5)
6 Intermittent (8)

8 Fairy (4)
11 Unlike (9)
14 Agitate (4)
16 Act (4)
18 Shoal (4)
21 Minus (8)
23 Want (4)
25 Arrive (4)
26 Sketched (4)

29 Revised (6)
30 Agreement (6)
32 Flower (5)
34 Close (4)
36 Twine (4)
40 Favourite (3)

132

ACROSS

1 Evaded (6)
5 Nursed (6)
9 Sound (5)
10 Interfere (6)
11 Abuse (6)
12 Send (5)
14 Scorch (4)
17 Father (3)
18 Lake (4)
20 Sharpened (5)
22 Foot-lever (5)
23 Bragged (7)
24 Number (5)
26 Paddled (5)
29 Image (4)
30 Youth (3)
32 Thoroughfare (4)
33 Claw (5)
35 Chose (6)
36 Publicised (6)
37 Apportion (5)
38 Stand (6)
39 Indeed (6)

DOWN

1 Disconnect (6)
2 Lower (6)
3 Always (4)
4 Ventured (5)
5 Shy (5)
6 Revise (4)
7 Plastered (6)
8 Fuel (6)
13 Assemble (7)
15 Trusted (5)
16 Revolt (5)
18 Decoration (5)
19 Bird (5)
21 Fellow (3)
22 Church-seat (3)
24 Easy (6)
25 Aired (6)
27 Girl (6)
28 Lethal (6)
30 Spoon (5)
31 Giver (5)
33 Rip (4)
34 Observe (4)

Evening Standard

133

ACROSS

3 Sail-boat (5)
9 Refuse (6)
10 Sick (6)
11 Blemish (5)
12 Poke (4)
15 Part (4)
17 Tiresome (7)
20 Fasten (3)
21 Subsequently (5)
23 Toy (4)
25 Ripped (4)
26 Not ever (5)
28 Pig-pen (3)
30 Sketch (7)
33 Skin (4)
35 Cavity (4)
36 Prompt (5)
38 Dread (6)
39 Lecture (6)
40 Principle (5)

DOWN

1 Slumbered (5)
2 Endured (5)
3 Aye (3)
4 Sly (6)
5 Greet (4)
6 Can (3)
7 Guide (5)
8 Concur (5)
13 Rest (7)
14 Couch (5)
16 Prosaic (7)
18 Rescued (5)
19 Encountered (3)
22 Crude (5)
24 Tree (3)
27 Puzzle (6)
28 Flood (5)
29 Long (5)
31 Awaken (5)
32 Intended (5)
34 Present (4)
36 Decay (3)
37 Still (3)

134

ACROSS

1 Portray (6)
5 Scrutinise (4)
8 Contact (5)
9 Also (3)
10 Flat (4)
11 Lame (4)
12 Advantage (5)

13 Spoil (6)
16 Sea-bird (4)
18 Sinful (4)
20 Deed (3)
22 Rug (3)
23 Barrier (3)
24 Singer (4)
25 Detail (4)
28 Harm (6)

30 Initial (5)
32 Fashionable (4)
33 Jot (4)
34 Wrath (3)
35 Material (5)
36 Stagger (4)
37 Sitting (6)

DOWN

1 Hold (6)
2 View (8)
3 Belief (6)
4 Agreed (9)
5 Planned (7)
6 Talk (4)
7 Observe (4)

8 Beverage (3)
14 Forgiveness (9)
15 Vigour (3)
17 Rodent (3)
19 Holiday (8)
20 Everything (3)
21 Current (7)
26 Run (6)

27 Ebb (6)
29 Blemish (4)
30 Blaze (4)
31 Weight (3)

Evening Standard

135

ACROSS

1 Pulverise (5)
5 Simpler (6)
8 Weary (5)
10 Scold (6)
11 Parched (4)
14 Spite (6)
15 Erased (7)

DOWN

2 Regret (3)
3 Said (6)
4 Strike (3)
5 Cheese (4)
6 Dirty (6)
7 Disclose (6)
9 Renovation (7)

18 For each (3)
19 Marry (3)
21 Dale (4)
23 Yawned (5)
24 Grasped (4)
27 Fate (3)
29 Sicken (3)
31 Tread (7)
32 Objective (6)

12 Knock (3)
13 Dreadful (4)
16 Sea-eagle (4)
17 Storehouse (5)
20 Take away (7)
22 Lounge (4)
24 Loathing (6)
25 Fat (4)
26 Summary (6)

34 Caribou (4)
35 Fold (6)
38 Performed (5)
39 Adroitly (6)
40 Trivial (5)

28 Hinder (6)
30 Shelter (3)
33 Salver (4)
36 Material (3)
37 Fixed (3)

136

ACROSS

2 Performed (5)
7 Healthy (4)
8 Get (6)
9 Lax (5)
11 Favourite (3)
13 Top (3)
15 Seepage (4)
16 Father (3)
18 Unaccompani-
ed (4)
19 Widespread
(7)
20 Near (4)
22 Surfeit (4)
23 Generous (7)
25 Stretched (4)
27 Beam (3)
28 Pain (4)
30 Performed (3)
31 Cask (3)
33 Ascend (5)
36 Stableman (6)
37 Off (4)
38 Cede (5)

DOWN

1 Skirmish (5)
2 Everything (3)
3 Also (3)
4 Rabbit (3)
5 Consumed (3)
6 Last (5)
10 Scrutinise (4)
11 Plotted (7)
12 Twisted (7)
13 Gather (7)
14 Mailmen (7)
16 Dissuade (5)
17 Postpone (5)
18 Droop (3)
21 Concealed (3)
24 Bar (4)
26 Booth (5)
29 Mortal (5)
32 Beer (3)
33 Weep (3)
34 Wrath (3)
35 Wicked (3)

Evening Standard

137

ACROSS

2 Breadth (5)
7 Vapour (5)
8 Allude (5)
10 Observed (5)
12 Cover (3)
13 Rasp (5)
15 Famed (7)
17 Ebb (6)
19 Unhappy (3)
20 Died (7)
23 Cupid (4)
25 Dreadful (4)
26 Purified (7)
30 Rug (3)
31 Scorn (6)
34 Lived (7)
37 Leaf (5)
38 Managed (3)
39 Sag (5)
40 Reimburse (5)
41 Drain (5)
42 Drive (5)

DOWN

1 Stock (5)
2 Squander (5)
3 Hinder (6)
4 Rank (4)
5 Deceived (7)
6 Yielded (5)
9 Healthy (3)
11 Wished (7)
13 Avarice (5)
14 Performer (5)
16 Equality (3)
18 Aroused (7)
21 Number (5)
22 Flat (5)
24 Course (7)
27 Whim (3)
28 Oust (6)
29 Cap (5)
32 Repulse (5)
33 Old-fashioned (5)
35 Weaken (3)
36 Beat (4)

138

ACROSS

1 Still (4)
4 Jostle (3)
6 Pace (4)
8 Suppose (6)
9 Display (6)
10 Fish-eggs (3)
12 Intended (5)
14 Blithe (5)
15 Keen (5)
18 Span (6)
20 Combined (6)
24 Booby-trapped (5)
26 Wrath (5)
28 Weary (5)
30 Finish (3)
32 Ornate (6)
33 Sooner (6)
34 Agitate (4)
35 Yelp (3)
36 Shrewd (4)

DOWN

2 Passage (5)
3 Lamented (7)
4 Scoff (4)
5 Yawn (4)
6 Rush (5)
7 Approve (7)
11 Mineral (3)
12 Crowd (3)
13 Label (3)
16 Jewel (3)
17 Manage (3)
19 Curl (7)
21 Entrap (3)
22 Foolish (7)
23 Defective (3)
25 Tavern (3)
27 Mistake (5)
29 Evict (5)
30 Whirlpool (4)
31 Ooze (4)

139

ACROSS

1 Feverish (6)
5 Spoke (6)
8 Solitary (8)
9 Circle (4)
10 Pig-pen (3)
12 Condition (5)
15 Offer (3)
17 Abroad (3)
18 Expert (3)
19 Bird (3)
20 Complete (5)
21 Ocean (3)
22 Sister (3)
23 Fasten (3)
24 Mat (3)
26 Flashlight (5)
29 Child (3)
33 Margin (4)
34 Lamented (8)
35 Bomb-hole (6)
36 Property (6)

DOWN

2 Upright (5)
3 Implement (4)
4 Map (5)
5 Handle (5)
6 Fat (4)
7 Boredom (5)
10 Guide (5)
11 Youthful (5)
12 Feat (5)
13 Change (5)
14 Ground (5)
15 Beleaguer (5)
16 Sketch (5)
25 Beneath (5)
27 Command (5)
28 Coppice (5)
30 Open (5)
31 Crooked (4)
32 Vanquish (4)

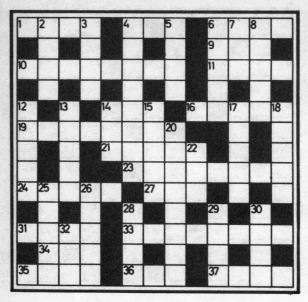

140

ACROSS

1 Spoken (4)
4 Stitch (3)
6 Candid (4)
9 Marshland (3)
10 Opposite (8)
11 Acid (4)
14 Cushion (3)
16 Fish (5)
19 Saviour (8)
21 Revolt (5)
23 Confirmed (8)
24 Mix (5)
27 Tear (3)
31 Remedy (4)
33 Eastern (8)
34 Owing (3)
35 Observed (4)
36 Silence (3)
37 Divide (4)

DOWN

2 Castle (4)
3 Adore (4)
4 Pennon (8)
5 Cry (4)
6 Frequently (5)
7 Vegetable (3)
8 Enlist (5)
12 Vision (5)
13 Viper (5)
14 For each (3)
15 Prevent (5)
17 Seed (5)
18 Dodge (5)
20 Shy (8)
22 Edge (3)
25 Ooze (5)
26 Verdant (5)
28 Lengthy (4)
29 Break (4)
30 Just (4)
32 Regret (3)

Evening Standard

141

ACROSS

4 Wed (5)
7 Demanding (6)
9 Cot (3)
10 Father (3)
12 Aristocratic (5)
13 Paradise (4)
15 Animal (5)
17 Discount (6)
19 Observe (4)
20 Saying (5)
22 Epoch (3)
24 Flood (7)
27 Edge (3)
28 Command (5)
31 Region (4)
33 Meal (6)
35 View (5)
37 Murder (4)
38 Share (5)
39 Fish (3)
41 Irritate (3)
42 Erase (6)
43 Kind (5)

DOWN

1 Current (6)
2 Skilful (6)
3 Finish (3)
4 Food-list (4)
5 Decorate (5)
6 Relation (8)
8 Fete (4)
11 Decide (9)
14 After deductions (4)
16 Lake (4)
18 Lout (4)
21 Opening (8)
23 Soon (4)
25 Travel (4)
26 Journey (4)
29 Motorist (6)
30 Wave (6)
32 Moving (5)
34 Want (4)
36 Attention (4)
40 Guided (3)

142

ACROSS

1 Increase (6)
5 Defeated (6)
9 Wandered (5)
10 Keep (6)
11 Talented (6)
12 Excellence (5)
14 Appear (4)
17 Lair (3)
18 Present (4)
20 Loathed (5)
22 Uncovered (5)
23 Swollen (7)
24 Unsoiled (5)
26 Principle (5)
29 Genuine (4)
30 Marry (3)
32 Tender (4)
33 Jockey (5)
35 Seller (6)
36 Objective (6)
37 Bar (5)
38 Evaded (6)
39 Hired (6)

DOWN

1 Gaudy (6)
2 Vent (6)
3 Spruce (4)
4 Sharpened (5)
5 Start (5)
6 Revise (4)
7 Reel (6)
8 Elbowed (6)
13 Eased (7)
15 Bird (5)
16 Decoration (5)
18 Hell (5)
19 Allude (5)
21 Noise (3)
22 Wager (3)
24 Desired (6)
25 Deserved (6)
27 Nothing (6)
28 Tried (6)
30 Cabled (5)
31 Dissuade (5)
33 Part (4)
34 Unusual (4)

Evening Standard

143

ACROSS

3 Lawful (5)
9 Loathing (6)
10 Disappear (6)
11 Weary (5)
12 Facts (4)
15 Roster (4)
17 Built (7)

20 Knock (3)
21 Attire (5)
23 Press (4)
25 Couple (4)
26 Inflexible (5)
28 Artful (3)
30 Denied (7)
33 Nobleman (4)
35 Naked (4)

36 Outcoming (5)
38 Swollen (6)
39 Stew (6)
40 Postpone (5)

DOWN

1 Scold (5)
2 Condition (5)
3 Permit (3)
4 Revised (6)
5 Declare (4)
6 Youth (3)
7 Lesser (5)

8 Inexpensive (5)
13 Thing (7)
14 Performer (5)
16 Lingered (7)
18 Sewer (5)
19 Serpent (3)
22 Devil (5)
24 Pinch (3)
27 Modest (6)

28 Flood (5)
29 Long (5)
31 Teacher (5)
32 Demise (5)
34 Yield (4)
36 Performed (3)
37 Sailor (3)

144

ACROSS

1 Grab (6)
5 Dross (4)
8 Contact (5)
9 Groove (3)
10 Satellite (4)
11 Vestibule (4)
12 Tender (5)
13 Moment (6)
16 Network (4)
18 Cheese (4)
20 For each (3)
22 Mineral (3)
23 Obscure (3)
24 Blaze (4)
25 Repair (4)
28 Mood (6)
30 Evade (5)
32 Reign (4)
33 Singer (4)
34 Child (3)
35 Harsh (5)
36 Mirth (4)
37 Guide (6)

DOWN

1 Emphasis (6)
2 Assailant (8)
3 Arrival (6)
4 Assured (9)
5 Planned (7)
6 Scorch (4)
7 Thaw (4)
8 Also (3)
14 Camel (9)
15 Butt (3)
17 Wrath (3)
19 Argued (8)
20 Mine (3)
21 Full (7)
26 Relegate (6)
27 Bomb-hole (6)
29 Boast (4)
30 Otherwise (4)
31 Moose (3)

Evening Standard

145

ACROSS

1 Lariat (5)
5 Squalid (6)
8 Perfect (5)
10 Sailors (6)
11 Sign (4)
14 Gift (6)
15 Rebuked (7)

DOWN

2 Imitate (3)
3 Easy (6)
4 Poem (3)
5 Aperture (4)
6 Staggered (6)
7 Pronouncement (6)

18 Beverage (3)
19 Colour (3)
21 Beat (4)
23 Revolt (5)
24 Carry (4)
27 Immerse (3)
29 Jewel (3)
31 Disarranged (7)

9 Penetrated (7)
12 Rug (3)
13 Close (4)
16 Centre (4)
17 Liability (5)
20 Ousted (7)
22 Impel (4)
24 Mendicant (6)
25 Fever (4)

32 Estimated (6)
34 Sea-eagle (4)
35 Evaded (6)
38 Sea-duck (5)
39 Rota (6)
40 Species (5)

26 Rue (6)
28 Promise (6)
30 Males (3)
33 Animal (4)
36 Limb (3)
37 Bird (3)

146

ACROSS

- **2** Kindle (5)
- **7** Nil (4)
- **8** Really (6)
- **9** Kind (5)
- **11** Fixed (3)
- **13** Tooth (3)
- **15** Cot (4)
- **16** Equality (3)
- **18** Tender (4)
- **19** Number (7)
- **20** Border (4)
- **22** Surfeit (4)
- **23** Terse (7)
- **25** Pitcher (4)
- **27** Dined (3)
- **28** Leer (4)
- **30** Performed (3)
- **31** Fish (3)
- **33** Booth (5)
- **36** Clerk (6)
- **37** Therefore (4)
- **38** Jam (5)

DOWN

- **1** Cut (5)
- **2** Record (3)
- **3** Firearm (3)
- **4** Fasten (3)
- **5** Uneven (3)
- **6** Singer (5)
- **10** Thoroughfare (4)
- **11** Twisted (7)
- **12** Thrilled (7)
- **13** School (7)
- **14** Refined (7)
- **16** Evidence (5)
- **17** Inflexible (5)
- **18** Droop (3)
- **21** Spike (3)
- **24** Tidy (4)
- **26** Flinch (5)
- **29** Shelf (5)
- **32** Intelligence (3)
- **33** Stitch (3)
- **34** Append (3)
- **35** Shelter (3)

Evening Standard

147

ACROSS

2 Order (5)
7 Extra (5)
8 Renovate (5)
10 Shaver (5)
12 Rim (3)
13 Performer (5)
15 Polluted (7)

DOWN

1 Room (5)
2 Mistake (5)
3 Scarcity (6)
4 Turf (4)
5 Charm (7)
6 Repulse (5)
9 Nothing (3)

17 Enthusiastic (6)
19 Hog (3)
20 Sound (7)
23 Between (4)
25 Ripped (4)
26 Lingered (7)
30 Male (3)
31 Loathe (6)

11 Responded (7)
13 Leading (5)
14 Implicit (5)
16 Meet (3)
18 Longed (7)
21 Rustic (5)
22 Combine (5)
24 Harmed (7)
27 Butt (3)

34 Visionary (7)
37 Worth (5)
38 Sack (3)
39 Satan (5)
40 Subsequently (5)
41 Work out (5)
42 Verdant (5)

28 Invent (6)
29 Of towns (5)
32 Claw (5)
33 Urbane (5)
35 Consume (3)
36 Breed (4)

148

ACROSS

1 Smack (4)
4 Wicked (3)
6 Denomination (4)
8 Sullen (6)
9 Sick (6)
10 Tease (3)
12 Under (5)
14 Postpone (5)
15 Domesticated (5)
18 Venerate (6)
20 Simply (6)
24 Taut (5)
26 Fun (5)
28 Centre (5)
30 Poem (3)
32 Bigger (6)
33 Plan (6)
34 Formerly (4)
35 Ballad (3)
36 Expensive (4)

DOWN

2 Lax (5)
3 Advance (7)
4 Ale (4)
5 Haul (4)
6 Ointment (5)
7 Hide (7)
11 Wonder (3)
12 Ban (3)
13 Conflict (3)
16 Encountered (3)
17 Lair (3)
19 Elucidate (7)
21 Tree (3)
22 Boiled (7)
23 Still (3)
25 Finish (3)
27 Rascal (5)
29 Dance (5)
30 Spoken (4)
31 Notice (4)

Evening Standard

149

ACROSS

1 Bargain (6)
5 Spanner (6)
8 Prevailing (8)
9 Mature (4)
10 Uncooked (3)
12 Map (5)
15 Parched (3)

DOWN

2 Fragrance (5)
3 End (4)
4 Attain (5)
5 Irrigate (5)
6 Nobleman (4)
7 Antic (5)
10 Wireless (5)

17 Lubricate (3)
18 Expert (3)
19 Obscure (3)
20 Perfect (5)
21 Imitate (3)
22 Tree (3)
23 Fate (3)
24 Possess (3)
26 Poorly (5)

11 Females (5)
12 Scale (5)
13 Correct (5)
14 Agree (5)
15 Demise (5)
16 Cede (5)
25 Complete (5)
27 Change (5)
28 Big (5)

29 Brick-carrier (3)
33 Kind (4)
34 Tormented (8)
35 Custodian (6)
36 Property (6)

30 Open (5)
31 Cease (4)
32 Fair (4)

150

ACROSS

1 Go by (4)
4 Intimidate (3)
6 Girdle (4)
9 Mine (3)
10 Persuade (8)
11 Image (4)
14 Coat (3)

DOWN

2 Soon (4)
3 Rescue (4)
4 Ate (8)
5 Cry (4)
6 Backbone (5)
7 Help (3)
8 Purloined (5)

16 Spree (5)
19 Pennon (8)
21 Fiend (5)
23 Decrease (8)
24 Vision (5)
27 Faucet (3)
31 Coating (4)
33 Inside (8)
34 Observe (3)

12 Enquired (5)
13 Commerce (5)
14 Whim (3)
15 Send (5)
17 Sound (5)
18 Supple (5)
20 Amorous (8)
22 Pinch (3)
25 Elevate (5)

35 Perused (4)
36 Curve (3)
37 Penniless (4)

26 Pointed (5)
28 Primadonna (4)
29 Fall (4)
30 Unaccompanied (4)
32 Meadow (3)

Evening Standard

151

ACROSS

4 Begin (5)
7 See-saw (6)
9 Sorrow (3)
10 Deity (3)
12 Depart (5)
13 Excuse (4)
15 Beleaguer (5)
17 Detain (6)
19 Hades (4)
20 Round-up (5)
22 Maul (3)
24 Maintained (7)
27 Spike (3)
28 Memorise (5)
31 Dagger (4)
33 Pill (6)
35 Reverence (5)
37 Position (4)
38 Prevent (5)
39 Stray (3)
41 Rank (3)
42 Simpler (6)
43 Pale (5)

DOWN

1 Daze (6)
2 Decapitate (6)
3 Fix (3)
4 Only (4)
5 Cogs (5)
6 Hand-gun (8)
8 Gown (4)
11 Hopeless (9)
14 Region (4)
16 Deer (4)
18 Part (4)
21 Abroad (8)
23 Healthy (4)
25 Tardy (4)
26 Intense (4)
29 Nuclear (6)
30 Character (6)
32 Extra (5)
34 Cowshed (4)
36 Press (4)
40 Butt (3)

152

ACROSS

1 Best (6)
5 Bully (6)
9 Heaped (5)
10 Tidier (6)
11 Coming (6)
12 Disparage (5)
14 Prophet (4)

17 Father (3)
18 Ale (4)
20 Hell (5)
22 Loaded (5)
23 Seaman (7)
24 Garret (5)
26 Lukewarm (5)
29 Closed (4)
30 Married (3)

32 Caribou (4)
33 Foul (5)
35 Disregard (6)
36 Deadened (6)
37 Bordered (5)
38 Nakedness (6)
39 Erase (6)

DOWN

1 End (6)
2 Approached (6)
3 Rushed (4)
4 Weary (5)
5 Learnt (5)
6 Whirlpool (4)

7 Poured (6)
8 Revert (6)
13 Showcase (7)
15 Ground (5)
16 Send (5)
18 Uncovered (5)
19 Weird (5)
21 Pouch (3)
22 Permit (3)

24 Appoint (6)
25 Rotated (6)
27 Stone (6)
28 Menial (6)
30 Thin (5)
31 Ate (5)
33 Worry (4)
34 Dandy (4)

Evening Standard

153

ACROSS

3 Upright (5)
9 Fruit (6)
10 Lasso (6)
11 Sea (5)
12 Thought (4)
15 Table (4)
17 Range (7)
20 Consumed (3)
21 Scour (5)
23 Genuine (4)
25 Otherwise (4)
26 Spoon (5)
28 Saying (3)
30 Sideboard (7)
33 Again (4)
35 Season (4)
36 Swift (5)
38 Rue (6)
39 Fuss (6)
40 Faded (5)

DOWN

1 Pick-me-up (5)
2 Seraglio (5)
3 Self (3)
4 Niche (6)
5 Talon (4)
6 Brown (3)
7 Shinbone (5)
8 Condition (5)
13 Commissiona-ire (7)
14 Horrify (5)
16 Guided (7)
18 Berate (5)
19 Owing (3)
22 Explosion (5)
24 Youth (3)
27 Fur (6)
28 Sword (5)
29 Jam (5)
31 Scorch (5)
32 Allude (5)
34 Facts (4)
36 Material (3)
37 Performed (3)

154

ACROSS

1 Clerk (6)
5 Staunch (4)
8 Drain (5)
9 Tank (3)
10 Ogle (4)
11 Remedy (4)
12 Dispute (5)

13 Swung (6)
16 Stable (4)
18 Flat (4)
20 Insect (3)
22 Prosecute (3)
23 Lair (3)
24 Singer (4)
25 Hang (4)
28 Reel (6)

30 Demon (5)
32 Fashionable (4)
33 Please (4)
34 Manage (3)
35 Idled (5)
36 Boring (4)
37 Span (6)

DOWN

1 Strict (6)
2 Reserved (8)
3 Faith (6)
4 Mirth (9)
5 Obtained (7)
6 Loyal (4)
7 Encounter (4)

8 Ocean (3)
14 Administered (9)
15 Males (3)
17 Regret (3)
19 Dared (8)
20 Mountain (3)
21 Current (7)
26 Physician (6)

27 Fawn (6)
29 Tart (4)
30 Occupy (4)
31 Defective (3)

Evening Standard

155

ACROSS

1 Fight (5)
5 Lithe (6)
8 Coppice (5)
10 Harm (6)
11 Imitated (4)
14 Pester (6)
15 Mislead (7)
18 Beverage (3)
19 Finish (3)
21 Cart (4)
23 Mistake (5)
24 Unfortunately (4)
27 Weight (3)
29 Tease (3)
31 Lamp (7)
32 Motorist (6)
34 Fruit (4)
35 Deserved (6)
38 Elbow (5)
39 Gift (6)
40 Enlighten (5)

DOWN

2 Meadow (3)
3 Frightened (6)
4 Pig (3)
5 Join (4)
6 Stripped (6)
7 Coarse (6)
9 Corrupt (7)
12 Tankard (3)
13 Expensive (4)
16 Wicked (4)
17 Enlist (5)
20 Given (7)
22 Declare (4)
24 Passionate (6)
25 Parched (4)
26 Ferocious (6)
28 Stocked (6)
30 Obtain (3)
33 Torn (4)
36 Era (3)
37 Sprite (3)

156

ACROSS

2 Performer (5)
7 Spoken (4)
8 Uncertain (6)
9 Restrict (5)
11 Dog (3)
13 Rotter (3)
15 Candid (4)
16 Lettuce (3)
18 Lot (4)
19 Free (7)
20 Detail (4)
22 Therefore (4)
23 Guard (7)
25 So be it (4)
27 Owing (3)
28 Present (4)
30 Cover (3)
31 Defective (3)
33 Jam (5)
36 Discussion (6)
37 Want (4)
38 Tendency (5)

DOWN

1 Set (5)
2 Everything (3)
3 Cat (3)
4 Groove (3)
5 Enquire (3)
6 Huge (5)
10 Image (4)
11 Funny (7)
12 Ebbed (7)
13 Borne (7)
14 Signified (7)
16 Yielded (5)
17 Because (5)
18 Charge (3)
21 Males (3)
24 Naked (4)
26 Collier (5)
29 Sovereign (5)
32 Evil (3)
33 Damp (3)
34 Expire (3)
35 Finish (3)

Evening Standard ════

157

ACROSS

2 Begin (5)
7 Condition (5)
8 Fruit (5)
10 Go in (5)
12 Vehicle (3)
13 Wrinkled (5)
15 Scorned (7)
17 Worn (6)
19 Youth (3)
20 Swelled (7)
23 Watched (4)
25 Finished (4)
26 Invented (7)
30 Whim (3)
31 Erase (6)
34 Aroused (7)
37 Lesser (5)
38 Brown (3)
39 Devil (5)
40 Cash (5)
41 Instruct (5)
42 Guide (5)

DOWN

1 Step (5)
2 War-horse (5)
3 Nursed (6)
4 Regretted (4)
5 Determined (7)
6 Drilled (5)
9 Insane (3)
11 Eased (7)
13 Bar (5)
14 Famous (5)
16 Rodent (3)
18 Parted (7)
21 Twelve (5)
22 Drain (5)
24 Delineated (7)
27 Tank (3)
28 Relegate (6)
29 Praise (5)
32 Ship (5)
33 Flashlight (5)
35 Tin (3)
36 Adroit (4)

158

ACROSS

1 Divide (4)
4 Intelligence (3)
6 Choose (4)
8 Celebrated (6)
9 Mad (6)
10 Faucet (3)
12 Under (5)
14 Stitched (5)
15 Lax (5)
18 Offer (6)
20 Ally (6)
24 Consumed (5)
26 Fun (5)
28 Dawdle (5)
30 Marshland (3)
32 Approval (6)
33 Riddle (6)
34 One (4)
35 Child (3)
36 Story (4)

DOWN

2 Astonish (5)
3 Double (7)
4 Direction (4)
5 Excursion (4)
6 Adhesive (5)
7 Interest (7)
11 Donkey (3)
12 Club (3)
13 Sorrow (3)
16 Mineral (3)
17 Newt (3)
19 Elucidate (7)
21 Colour (3)
22 Silliness (7)
23 Arid (3)
25 Expert (3)
27 Perch (5)
29 Animal (5)
30 Worry (4)
31 Tidy (4)

Evening Standard

159

ACROSS

1 Fiery (6)
5 Small (6)
8 Agreeable (8)
9 Unusual (4)
10 Strange (3)
12 Challenged (5)
15 Favourite (3)
17 Stray (3)
18 Sick (3)
19 Epoch (3)
20 Sea-duck (5)
21 Astern (3)
22 Record (3)
23 Firearm (3)
24 Consume (3)
26 Stock (5)
29 Number (3)
33 Cease (4)
34 Deduct (8)
35 Span (6)
36 Fall (6)

DOWN

2 Lubricated (5)
3 Back (4)
4 Play (5)
5 Supple (5)
6 Weary (4)
7 Big (5)
10 Fat (5)
11 Traded (5)
12 Lees (5)
13 Wireless (5)
14 Lament (5)
15 Factory (5)
16 Giant (5)
25 Change (5)
27 Flavour (5)
28 Refute (5)
30 Surpass (5)
31 Rushed (4)
32 Terrible (4)

160

ACROSS

1 Grasp (4)
4 Immerse (3)
6 Money (4)
9 Fitting (3)
10 Keep (8)
11 Tolerate (4)
14 Deed (3)
16 Allude (5)
19 Unearth (8)
21 Principle (5)
23 Rule (8)
24 Soar (5)
27 Managed (3)
31 Object (4)
33 Similarity (8)
34 Strive (3)
35 Unite (4)
36 Cushion (3)
37 Team (4)

DOWN

2 Castle (4)
3 Overtake (4)
4 Ordered (8)
5 Nobleman (4)
6 Wire (5)
7 Imitate (3)
8 Musty (5)
12 Confess (5)
13 Awry (5)
14 Insect (3)
15 Singer (5)
17 Last (5)
18 Mature (5)
20 Mentioned (8)
22 Can (3)
25 Fruit (5)
26 Finished (5)
28 Smack (4)
29 Responsibility (4)
30 Employed (4)
32 Nothing (3)

Evening Standard

ACROSS

4 Vestibule (5)
7 Anew (6)
9 Rug (3)
10 Vigour (3)
12 Form (5)
13 Spoken (4)
15 Originate (5)

17 Smart (6)
19 Attack (4)
20 Step (5)
22 Drunkard (3)
24 Matured (7)
27 Males (3)
28 Sordid (5)
31 Defeat (4)
33 Expressed (6)

35 Irrigate (5)
37 Puppet (4)
38 Sudden fear (5)
39 Immerse (3)
41 Pinch (3)
42 Erase (6)
43 Yielded (5)

DOWN

1 Noted (6)
2 Fleet (6)
3 Snake (3)
4 Spend (4)
5 Alternative (5)
6 Pepper (8)
8 Pile (4)

11 Offered (9)
14 Den (4)
16 Press (4)
18 Precise (4)
21 Endure (8)
23 Trial (4)
25 Plague (4)
26 Act (4)
29 Worshipped (6)

30 Shouted (6)
32 String (5)
34 Parched (4)
36 Tart (4)
40 Favourite (3)

162

ACROSS

1 Niche (6)
5 Fruit (6)
9 Consumer (5)
10 Quiet (6)
11 Sex (6)
12 Shinbone (5)
14 Cheese (4)
17 Sister (3)
18 Remedy (4)
20 Challenged (5)
22 Cabled (5)
23 Curl (7)
24 Foul (5)
26 Dissuade (5)
29 Revise (4)
30 Number (3)
32 Valley (4)
33 Decoration (5)
35 Allowance (6)
36 Human (6)
37 Elector (5)
38 Totter (6)
39 Rely (6)

DOWN

1 Reposed (6)
2 Vault (6)
3 Despatched (4)
4 Material (5)
5 Start (5)
6 Region (4)
7 Passion (6)
8 Concurred (6)
13 Botched (7)
15 Old-fashioned (5)
16 Deserve (5)
18 Quoted (5)
19 Spree (5)
21 Performed (3)
22 Marry (3)
24 Dreaded (6)
25 Coloured (6)
27 Gossip (6)
28 Staggered (6)
30 Singer (5)
31 Called (5)
33 Stir (4)
34 Learning (4)

Evening Standard

163

ACROSS

3 Afterwards (5)
9 Beast (6)
10 Cope (6)
11 Unadorned (5)
12 Flag (4)
15 Swimming-pool (4)
17 Fixed (7)
20 Lair (3)
21 Trench (5)
23 Curse (4)
25 Story (4)
26 Keen (5)
28 Tiny (3)
30 Wished (7)
33 Sea-eagle (4)
35 Season (4)
36 Garret (5)
38 Lubricate (6)
39 Gift (6)
40 Rate (5)

DOWN

1 Foundation (5)
2 Restrict (5)
3 Circuit (3)
4 United (6)
5 Discharge (4)
6 Raced (3)
7 Swift (5)
8 Fiend (5)
13 Regain (7)
14 Condition (5)
16 Erased (7)
18 Plunged (5)
19 Deed (3)
22 Custom (5)
24 Owned (3)
27 Read out (6)
28 Jam (5)
29 Go in (5)
31 Jockey (5)
32 Demise (5)
34 Pace (4)
36 Donkey (3)
37 Rotter (3)

164

ACROSS

1 Maniac (6)
5 Donkey (4)
8 Females (5)
9 Noise (3)
10 Animal (4)
11 Assistant (4)
12 Happening (5)

13 Season (6)
16 Nobleman (4)
18 Cupid (4)
20 Consumed (3)
22 Fixed (3)
23 Colour (3)
24 Bearing (4)
25 Excuse (4)
28 Imagined (6)

30 Comical (5)
32 Rip (4)
33 Unhearing (4)
34 Devil (3)
35 Principle (5)
36 Regretted (4)
37 Dip (6)

DOWN

1 Retiring (6)
2 Explosive (8)
3 Slumbering (6)
4 Changed (9)
5 Wander (7)
6 One (4)
7 Flat (4)

8 Sorrow (3)
14 Replied (9)
15 Brick-carrier (3)
17 Fish (3)
19 Relative (8)
20 Objective (3)
21 Bore (7)
26 Cunning (6)

27 Principal (6)
29 Agitate (4)
30 Lot (4)
31 Still (3)

Evening Standard

165

ACROSS

1 Waterway (5)
5 Habit (6)
8 Attend (5)
10 Pure (6)
11 Fate (4)
14 Wandering (6)
15 Antelope (7)

18 Cot (3)
19 Entrap (3)
21 Deceased (4)
23 Repulse (5)
24 Cook (4)
27 Obscure (3)
29 Joker (3)
31 Nominate (7)
32 Talented (6)

34 Roster (4)
35 Soaked (6)
38 Name (5)
39 Scanty (6)
40 Sketch (5)

DOWN

2 Tree (3)
3 Suppose (6)
4 Permit (3)
5 Yield (4)
6 Stocked (6)
7 Coined (6)
9 Purified (7)

12 Sphere (3)
13 Manufactured (4)
16 Quiet (4)
17 Brown (5)
20 Storm (7)
22 Related (4)
24 Prickly plant (6)

25 Pitcher (4)
26 Approval (6)
28 Meditate (6)
30 Obtain (3)
33 Speed (4)
36 Aged (3)
37 Sprite (3

166

ACROSS

2 Inflexible (5)
7 Impel (4)
8 Clamour (6)
9 Suspect (5)
11 Devil (3)
13 Vehicle (3)
15 Masculine (4)

16 Butt (3)
18 Nip (4)
19 Unaffected (7)
20 Crew (4)
22 Surfeit (4)
23 Observed (7)
25 Want (4)
27 Performed (3)

28 Prima donna (4)
30 Finish (3)
31 Nothing (3)
33 Memorise (5)
36 Forthcoming (6)
37 Discharge (4)
38 Hail (5)

DOWN

1 Play (5)
2 Colour (3)
3 Animal (3)
4 Spot (3)
5 Pig-pen (3)
6 Huge (5)
10 Defeat (4)

11 Fancy (7)
12 Plotted (7)
13 Scoundrel (7)
14 Unbiased (7)
16 Swift (5)
17 Quietened (5)
18 Sack (3)
21 Deity (3)
24 Quote (4)

26 Follow (5)
29 Call (5)
32 Mire (3)
33 Limb (3)
34 Imitate (3)
35 Entrap (3)

Evening Standard

167

ACROSS

2 Annoyance (5)
7 Vapour (5)
8 Prevent (5)
10 Haste (5)
12 Illuminated (3)
13 Rasp (5)
15 Discussed (7)
17 Ebb (6)
19 Obese (3)
20 Aroused (7)
23 Poke (4)
25 Adroit (4)
26 Purified (7)
30 Dog (3)
31 Scorn (6)
34 Wished (7)
37 Leaf (5)
38 Youth (3)
39 Sag (5)
40 Old-fashioned (5)
41 Feeling (5)
42 Drive (5)

DOWN

1 Stock (5)
2 Adhesive (5)
3 Hinder (6)
4 Employed (4)
5 Told (7)
6 Irrigate (5)
9 Scrap (3)
11 Delineated (7)
13 Feel (5)
14 Performer (5)
16 Club (3)
18 Died (7)
21 Liability (5)
22 Brace (5)
24 Determined (7)
27 Coat (3)
28 Oust (6)
29 Hindrance (5)
32 Repulse (5)
33 Flower (5)
35 Posed (3)
36 Beat (4)

168

ACROSS

1 Fashionable (4)
4 Beaker (3)
6 Fortune (4)
8 Rage (6)
9 Mad (6)
10 Lump (3)
12 Inclined (5)
14 Premium (5)
15 Keen (5)
18 Appear (6)
20 Combined (6)
24 Principle (5)
26 Employing (5)
28 Tired (5)
30 Drink (3)
32 Outlaw (6)
33 Memorised (6)
34 Yield (4)
35 Males (3)
36 Watched (4)

DOWN

2 Dwelling (5)
3 Singer (7)
4 Munch (4)
5 Settled (4)
6 Lariat (5)
7 Perplex (7)
11 Wonder (3)
12 Untruth (3)
13 Label (3)
16 Obtain (3)
17 Manage (3)
19 Error (7)
21 Novel (3)
22 Repeat (7)
23 Arid (3)
25 Bird (3)
27 Elbow (5)
29 Scope (5)
30 Staunch (4)
31 Scheme (4)

Evening Standard

169

ACROSS

1 Bet (6)
5 Stress (6)
8 Delineate (8)
9 Distribute (4)
10 Consumed (3)
12 Condition (5)
15 Menagerie (3)

17 Iota (3)
18 Hatchet (3)
19 Poem (3)
20 Beneath (5)
21 Prohibit (3)
22 Tin (3)
23 Hill (3)
24 Child (3)
26 Flashlight (5)

29 Beer (3)
33 Vessel (4)
34 Barter (8)
35 Span (6)
36 Anticipate (6)

DOWN

2 Vigilant (5)
3 Support (4)
4 Live (5)
5 Dulcet (5)
6 Discourteous (4)
7 Ice-house (5)

10 Concerning (5)
11 Evict (5)
12 Feat (5)
13 Viper (5)
14 Ground (5)
15 Animal (5)
16 Weight (5)
25 Alternative (5)
27 Fat (5)

28 Hide (5)
30 Reasoning (5)
31 Rushed (4)
32 Moist (4)

170

ACROSS

1 Reckless (4)
4 Sever (3)
6 Wine (4)
9 Charge (3)
10 Contemned (8)
11 Flavour (4)
14 Fish (3)
16 Avarice (5)
19 Pennon (8)
21 Reimburse (5)
23 Revolving (8)
24 Long (5)
27 Gratuity (3)
31 Chasm (4)
33 Agreement (8)
34 Shelter (3)
35 Asterisk (4)
36 Lubricate (3)
37 Repair (4)

DOWN

2 Top (4)
3 Trust (4)
4 Client (8)
5 Neat (4)
6 Later (5)
7 Ocean (3)
8 Taut (5)
12 Composition (5)
13 Fragrance (5)
14 Vehicle (3)
15 Storehouse (5)
17 Nest (5)
18 Evade (5)
20 Sane (8)
22 Yelp (3)
25 Triumph (5)
26 Allude (5)
28 Resound (4)
29 Terrible (4)
30 Scrutinise (4)
32 Meadow (3)

Evening Standard

ACROSS

4. Distribute (5)
7. Whole (6)
9. Tree (3)
10. Curve (3)
12. Lawful (5)
13. Increase (4)
15. New (5)
17. Placid (6)
19. Charge (4)
20. Name (5)
22. Healthy (3)
24. Polluted (7)
27. Father (3)
28. Poor (5)
31. Dingy (4)
33. Reposed (6)
35. Representative (5)
37. Face (4)
38. Condition (5)
39. Gratuity (3)
41. Headgear (3)
42. Ebb (6)
43. Viper (5)

DOWN

1. Stature (6)
2. Farthest (6)
3. Epoch (3)
4. Island (4)
5. Husk (5)
6. Undiminished (8)
8. Sea-eagle (4)
11. Assured (9)
14. Unite (4)
16. Mask (4)
18. Rush (4)
21. Repeated (8)
23. Marquee (4)
25. Food (4)
26. Act (4)
29. Revised (6)
30. Shouted (6)
32. Swim (5)
34. Agitate (4)
36. Equipment (4)
40. Enclosure (3)

172

ACROSS

1. Read (6)
5. Figurine (6)
9. Fish (5)
10. Greet (6)
11. Deserved (6)
12. Cinder (5)
14. Finished (4)
17. Yelp (3)
18. Breed (4)
20. Jockey (5)
22. Emblem (5)
23. Advantage (7)
24. War-horse (5)
26. Cap (5)
29. Lofty (4)
30. Groove (3)
32. Caribou (4)
33. Lubricated (5)
35. Performing (6)
36. Forgive (6)
37. Courteous (5)
38. Evaded (6)
39. Order (6)

DOWN

1 Clergyman (6)
2 Revolved (6)
3 Satisfy (4)
4 Foe (5)
5 Slumber (5)
6 Rip (4)
7 Nursed (6)
8 Bear (6)
13 Malignant (7)
15 View (5)
16 Revolt (5)
18 Assessed (5)
19 Concur (5)
21 Colour (3)
22 Child's clothes-protector (3)
24 Shore (6)
25 Exhilarated (6)
27 Give (6)
28 Coma (6)
30 Inflexible (5)
31 Lukewarm (5)
33 Formerly (4)
34 Valley (4)

Evening Standard

173

ACROSS

3. Flavour (5)
9. Pressed (6)
10. Insult (6)
11. Happening (5)
12. Region (4)
15. Retain (4)
17. Nunnery (7)

20. Rodent (3)
21. Weary (5)
23. Greedy (4)
25. Trade (4)
26. Sewer (5)
28. Deed (3)
30. Erased (7)
33. Consider (4)
35. Unusual (4)

36. View (5)
38. Recover (6)
39. Fur (6)
40. Blithe (5)

DOWN

1. Tree (5)
2. Symbol (5)
3. Golf-peg (3)
4. Coming (6)
5. Shade (4)
6. Newt (3)
7. Allude (5)

8. Skilful (5)
13. Affair (7)
14. Shun (5)
16. Sooner (7)
18. Shy (5)
19. Marry (3)
22. Postpone (5)
24. Parched (3)
27. Lower (6)

28. Worship (5)
29. Instruct (5)
31. Implicit (5)
32. Dissuade (5)
34. Mature (4)
36. Amount (3)
37. Attempt (3)

174

ACROSS

1. Although (6)
5. Exude (4)
8. Keen (5)
9. Sick (3)
10. Insect (4)
11. Expensive (4)
12. Tree (5)
13. Delay (6)
16. Lake (4)
18. Cheese (4)
20. Aged (3)
22. Tin (3)
23. Lair (3)
24. Rank (4)
25. Pitcher (4)
28. Dedicate (6)
30. Malice (5)
32. Excursion (4)
33. Just (4)
34. Astern (3)
35. Outcoming (5)
36. Expired (4)
37. Stick (6)

DOWN

1. Bird-house (6)
2. Disparage (8)
3. Feeble (6)
4. Disciplined (9)
5. Commanded (7)
6. Candid (4)
7. Nobleman (4)
8. Ocean (3)
14. Dishonest (9)
15. Brown (3)
17. Uncooked (3)
19. Adorn (8)
20. Lubricate (3)
21. Fell (7)
26. Bred (6)
27. Condition (6)
29. Fastener (4)
30. Team (4)
31. Consume (3)

Evening Standard

175

ACROSS

1 Vault (5)
5 Sun-bathed (6)
8 Deposit (5)
10 Strict (6)
11 Imitated (4)
14 Comment (6)
15 Pliable (7)

18 Obtain (3)
19 Gesture of assent (3)
21 Liability (4)
23 Fiend (5)
24 Pace (4)
27 Noise (3)
29 Tank (3)
31 Cautious (7)

32 Dirty (6)
34 Thoroughfare (4)
35 Evoke (6)
38 Paled (5)
39 Retiring (6)
40 Principle (5)

DOWN

2. Fish-eggs (3)
3. Delight (6)
4. Hill (3)
5. Endure (4)
6. Appeared (6)
7. Voucher (6)
9. Delineated (7)

12. Fix (3)
13. Fruit (4)
16. Raise (4)
17. Funny (5)
20. Gave (7)
22. Dandy (4)
24. Method (6)
25. Sinful (4)
26. Liking (6)

28. Determine (6)
30. Number (3)
33. Adroit (4)
36. Allow (3)
37. Wrath (3)

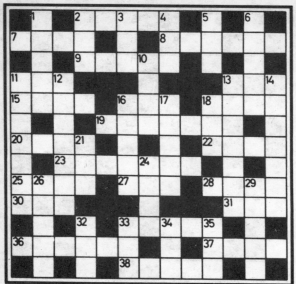

176

ACROSS

2 Grip (5)
7 Roster (4)
8 Shrewd (6)
9 Trivial (5)
11 Intimidate (3)
13 Free (3)
15 Spoken (4)

16 Tank (3)
18 Lake (4)
19 Wed (7)
20 Detail (4)
22 Air (4)
23 Unaffected (7)
25 Declare (4)
27 Consume (3)
28 Nothing (4)

30 Cover (3)
31 Immerse (3)
33 Unsighted (5)
36 Pace (6)
37 One (4)
38 Subject (5)

DOWN

1 Engine (5)
2 Interval (3)
3 Astern (3)
4 Wages (3)
5 Pig-pen (3)
6 Step (5)
10 Rip (4)

11 Funny (7)
12 Roused (7)
13 Diminished (7)
14 Evolve (7)
16 Obscure (5)
17 Handle (5)
18 Encountered (3)
21 Spoil (3)

24 Bar (4)
26 View (5)
29 Inflexible (5)
32 Gain (3)
33 Wager (3)
34 Wrath (3)
35 Owing (3)

Evening Standard ━━━

177

ACROSS

2 Upset (5)
7 Monarch (5)
8 Drain (5)
10 Elector (5)
12 Equality (3)
13 Sorrow (5)
15 Made fast (7)
17 Terrible (6)
19 Feline (3)
20 Soared (7)
23 Location (4)
25 Trade (4)
26 Betrothed (7)
30 Bed (3)
31 Relegate (6)
34 Guided (7)
37 Cash (5)
38 Insane (3)
39 Object (5)
40 Jockey (5)
41 Swift (5)
42 Fishing-basket (5)

DOWN

1 Donkey (5)
2 Cut (5)
3 Gain (6)
4 Dregs (4)
5 Famed (7)
6 Cap (5)
9 Conflict (3)
11 Ebbed (7)
13 Spectre (5)
14 Angry (5)
16 Vehicle (3)
18 Given (7)
21 Devil (5)
22 Passage (5)
24 Enciphered (7)
27 Obtained (3)
28 Modest (6)
29 Restrict (5)
32 Ethical (5)
33 Lukewarm (5)
35 Youth (3)
36 Expensive (4)

178

ACROSS

1 Fashionable (4)
4 Whim (3)
6 Cheat (4)
8 Gloomy (6)
9 Race (6)
10 Ballad (3)

12 Seat (5)
14 Intellect (5)
15 Prompt (5)
18 Placard (6)
20 Exhilarated (6)
24 Sum (5)
26 Because (5)
28 Clearing (5)

30 Finish (3)
32 Transgressed (6)
33 Recompense (6)
34 Shout (4)
35 Chart (3)
36 Intense (4)

DOWN

2 Lift (5)
3 Ease (7)
4 Dropped (4)
5 Repudiate (4)
6 Dissuade (5)
7 Undertake (7)
11 Help (3)

12 Mouthful (3)
13 Shelter (3)
16 Skill (3)
17 Still (3)
19 Aperture (7)
21 Loiter (3)
22 Permitted (7)
23 Expire (3)
25 Possess (3)

27 Waterway (5)
29 Lament (5)
30 Cheese (4)
31 Ooze (4)

Evening Standard ═══

179

ACROSS

1 Attic (6)
5 Collect (6)
8 Include (8)
9 Vanquish (4)
10 Unhappy (3)
12 Impression (5)
15 Fixed (3)
17 Moose (3)
18 Sort (3)
19 Sick (3)
20 Likeness (5)
21 Donkey (3)
22 Everything (3)
23 Sever (3)
24 Attempt (3)
26 Deposit (5)
29 Watch (3)
33 Dumb (4)
34 Numbed (8)
35 Offer (6)
36 Diatribe (6)

DOWN

2 Fragrance (5)
3 Mature (4)
4 Screw (5)
5 Glimmer (5)
6 Weary (4)
7 Ooze (5)
10 Rapid (5)
11 Postpone (5)
12 Art (5)
13 Prize (5)
14 Portion (5)
15 Fish (5)
16 Flavour (5)
25 Excite (5)
27 Command (5)
28 Allowance (5)
30 Cede (5)
31 Remit (4)
32 Ale (4)

180

ACROSS

1 Applaud (4)
4 Devil (3)
6 Parched (4)
9 Vehicle (3)
10 Gap (8)
11 Formerly (4)
14 Insect (3)
16 Worship (5)
19 Taken (8)
21 Principle (5)
23 Home (8)
24 Each (5)
27 Fish-eggs (3)
31 Worry (4)
33 Estrange (8)
34 Observe (3)
35 Unite (4)
36 Transgress (3)
37 Divide (4)

DOWN

2 Wrinkle (4)
3 Strip (4)
4 Devised (8)
5 Tug (4)
6 Shun (5)
7 Managed (3)
8 Provoke (5)
12 Emblem (5)
13 View (5)
14 Fitting (3)
15 Singer (5)
17 Refuge (5)
18 Eject (5)
20 Relegation (8)
22 Fasten (3)
25 Poetry (5)
26 Assessed (5)
28 Lump (4)
29 Break (4)
30 Agitate (4)
32 Fish (3)

Evening Standard

181

ACROSS

4 Slab (5)
7 Stripe (6)
9 Mineral (3)
10 Free (3)
12 Deflect (5)
13 Cheese (4)
15 Jam (5)

17 Pollute (6)
19 Hush (4)
20 Tool (5)
22 Tree (3)
24 Swung (7)
27 Beverage (3)
28 Perch (5)
31 Elderly (4)
33 Be there (6)

35 Irrigate (5)
37 Revise (4)
38 Jockey (5)
39 Immerse (3)
41 Cover (3)
42 Spirit (6)
43 Infant (5)

DOWN

1 Slumbering (6)
2 Fleet (6)
3 Scull (3)
4 Boast (4)
5 Flat (5)
6 Negligent (8)
8 Bird (4)

11 Deputed (9)
14 Repair (4)
16 Dale (4)
18 Exploit (4)
21 Faint (8)
23 Lake (4)
25 Tidy (4)
26 Finished (4)
29 Strangeness (6)

30 Reel (6)
32 Live (5)
34 Spruce (4)
36 Dry (4)
40 Favourite (3)

182

ACROSS

1 Stink (6)
5 Figurine (6)
9 Hurry (5)
10 Beat (6)
11 Loutish (6)
12 Reappear (5)
14 Lake (4)

17 Spot (3)
18 Yield (4)
20 Go in (5)
22 Dissipated (5)
23 Of clay (7)
24 Shabby (5)
26 Domesticated (5)
29 Salver (4)

30 Era (3)
32 Entice (4)
33 Tendency (5)
35 Meditate (6)
36 Disagree (6)
37 Loaded (5)
38 Discourteously (6)
39 Erase (6)

DOWN

1 Serene (6)
2 Exertion (6)
3 Scorch (4)
4 Loathed (5)
5 Fat (5)
6 Rip (4)
7 Followed (6)

8 Reverberated (6)
13 Dwelling (7)
15 Wrath (5)
16 Poor (5)
18 Waterway (5)
19 Postpone (5)
21 Beam (3)
22 Spout (3)

24 Coma (6)
25 Deserved (6)
27 Stifle (6)
28 Order (6)
30 Marshal (5)
31 Finished (5)
33 Inform (4)
34 Eat (4)

Evening Standard ═══

183

ACROSS

3 Torment (5)
9 Keep (6)
10 Embrace (6)
11 Walked (5)
12 Tart (4)
15 Spoken (4)
17 Eye-glass (7)

20 Beer (3)
21 Eject (5)
23 Idiot (4)
25 Food-list (4)
26 Wandered (5)
28 Donkey (3)
30 Reduced (7)
33 Employed (4)
35 Travel (4)

36 Shun (5)
38 Uncertain (6)
39 Hidden (6)
40 Attempted (5)

DOWN

1 Vision (5)
2 Blemish (5)
3 Gratuity (3)
4 Empower (6)
5 Pip (4)
6 Finish (3)
7 Snake (5)

8 Confuse (5)
13 Admit (7)
14 Giver (5)
16 Referred (7)
18 Surpass (5)
19 Border (3)
22 Bar (5)
24 Fortune (3)
27 Submissive (6)

28 Presage (5)
29 Feeling (5)
31 Stream (5)
32 Demise (5)
34 Assert (4)
36 Skill (3)
37 Father (3)

184

ACROSS

1 Recent (6)
5 Off (4)
8 Impel (5)
9 Sailor (3)
10 Animal (4)
11 Talon (4)
12 Bordered (5)
13 Followed (6)
16 Entertainment (4)
18 Otherwise (4)
20 Lettuce (3)
22 Vehicle (3)
23 Expire (3)
24 Hypocrisy (4)
25 Watched (4)
28 Proper (6)
30 Stupid (5)
32 Plan (4)
33 Detail (4)
34 Serpent (3)
35 Lure (5)
36 Want (4)
37 Stick (6)

DOWN

1 Stuff (6)
2 Scorn (8)
3 Assistance (6)
4 Censured (9)
5 Assented (7)
6 Unite (4)
7 Gape (4)
8 Enemy (3)
14 Amusement (9)
15 Employ (3)
17 Ballad (3)
19 Release (8)
20 Tin (3)
21 Began (7)
26 Considered (6)
27 Principal (6)
29 Candid (4)
30 Cipher (4)
31 Pig-pen (3)

Evening Standard

185

ACROSS

1 Sham (5)
5 Struggle (6)
8 Elbow (5)
10 Remitter (6)
11 Remain (4)
14 Gift (6)
15 Frenzied (7)
18 Vegetable (3)
19 Horse (3)
21 Cart (4)
23 Repulse (5)
24 Crowd (4)
27 Lair (3)
29 Fish (3)
31 Back (7)
32 Gloomy (6)
34 Cab (4)
35 Skilful (6)
38 Worth (5)
39 Irritate (6)
40 Strayed (5)

DOWN

2 Poem (3)
3 Unfastened (6)
4 Prosecute (3)
5 Trial (4)
6 Climbed (6)
7 Coarse (6)
9 Exhausted (7)
12 Faucet (3)
13 Annum (4)
16 Part (4)
17 Antic (5)
20 Widespread (7)
22 Unfortunately (4)
24 Concealed (6)
25 Repose (4)
26 Claim (6)
28 Carrier (6)
30 Loose (3)
33 Dwell (4)
36 Owing (3)
37 Wrath (3)

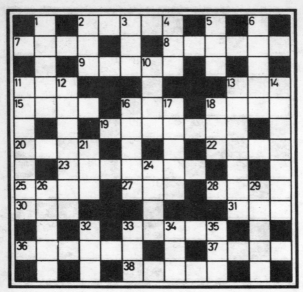

186

ACROSS

2 Fishing-basket (5)
7 Nil (4)
8 Arouse (6)
9 Traded (5)
11 Greeting (3)
13 Mire (3)
15 Marquee (4)
16 Golf-peg (3)
18 Entrance (4)
19 Errand (7)
20 Placed (4)
22 Cab (4)
23 Splendid (7)
25 Watched (4)
27 Age (3)
28 Lake (4)
30 Colour (3)
31 Performed (3)
33 Short (5)
36 Fawn (6)
37 Lament (4)
38 Elbow (5)

DOWN

1 Dig (5)
2 Fish (3)
3 Epoch (3)
4 Permit (3)
5 Deed (3)
6 Portly (5)
10 Dregs (4)
11 Studio (7)
12 Lured (7)
13 Ran (7)
14 Wished (7)
16 Shy (5)
17 Composition (5)
18 Obtained (3)
21 Father (3)
24 Domesticated (4)
26 Long (5)
29 Inflexible (5)
32 Writing-fluid (3)
33 Number (3)
34 Free (3)
35 Sheep (3)

Evening Standard

187

ACROSS

2 Scope (5)
7 Hell (5)
8 Guide (5)
10 Permit (5)
12 Present (3)
13 Jig (5)
15 Harmed (7)

17 Exhilarated (6)
19 Vehicle (3)
20 Power (7)
23 Frozen (4)
25 Nobleman (4)
26 Swelled (7)
30 Pose (3)
31 Darted (6)
34 Crime (7)

37 Wood-joint (5)
38 Meadow (3)
39 Couch (5)
40 Demand (5)
41 Twist (5)
42 Wager (5)

DOWN

1 Trite (5)
2 Respond (5)
3 Slumbering (6)
4 Righteous (4)
5 Funds (7)
6 Subdued (5)
9 Record (3)

11 Fluctuated (7)
13 Satan (5)
14 Nude (5)
16 Male (3)
18 Gave (7)
21 Sail-boat (5)
22 Evade (5)
24 Scorn (7)
27 Untruth (3)

28 Material (6)
29 Stupid (5)
32 Because (5)
33 Strayed (5)
35 Ocean (3)
36 Food (4)

188

ACROSS

1 Incline (4)
4 Cake (3)
6 Choose (4)
8 Corsair (6)
9 Beast (6)
10 Decay (3)
12 Zest (5)

14 Storehouse (5)
15 Silly (5)
18 Put (6)
20 Character (6)
24 Evade (5)
26 Combine (5)
28 Order (5)
30 Newt (3)
32 Claim (6)

33 Amatory (6)
34 Pace (4)
35 Silent (3)
36 Bogus (4)

DOWN

2 Goodbye (5)
3 Pliable (7)
4 Ale (4)
5 Tidy (4)
6 Cost (5)
7 Uproar (7)
11 Possess (3)

12 Breech (3)
13 Individual (3)
16 Append (3)
17 Finish (3)
19 Merciful (7)
21 Era (3)
22 Boring (7)
23 Consume (3)
25 Lout (3)

27 Vagrant (5)
29 Porcelain (5)
30 Cheese (4)
31 Side (4)

Evening Standard ═══

189

ACROSS

1 Niche (6)
5 Evade (6)
8 Outlook (8)
9 Smack (4)
10 Always (3)
12 Vision (5)
15 Obese (3)

DOWN

2 Premature (5)
3 Orient (4)
4 Guide (5)
5 Additional (5)
6 Price (4)
7 Square (5)
10 Advantage (5)

17 Wonder (3)
18 Sick (3)
19 Drunkard (3)
20 Booby-trapped (5)
21 Wrath (3)
22 Self (3)
23 Firearm (3)
24 Can (3)

11 Consumed (5)
12 Devil (5)
13 Boredom (5)
14 Insect (5)
15 Throw (5)
16 Trample (5)
25 Outcome (5)
27 Alternative (5)
28 Musty (5)

26 Din (5)
29 Deity (3)
33 Employed (4)
34 Promontory (8)
35 See-saw (6)
36 Skilful (6)

30 Proprietor (5)
31 Revise (4)
32 Applaud (4)

190

ACROSS

1 Worry (4)
4 Bed (3)
6 Barrel (4)
9 Strike (3)
10 Ate (8)
11 Unfortunately (4)
14 Fish (3)
16 Begin (5)
19 Journalist (8)
21 Spree (5)
23 Claimed (8)
24 Dulcet (5)
27 Beam (3)
31 Analyse (4)
33 Perpetual (8)
34 Also (3)
35 Sense (4)
36 Defective (3)
37 Conduit (4)

DOWN

2 Bird (4)
3 Trial (4)
4 Vied (8)
5 Neat (4)
6 Map (5)
7 Sicken (3)
8 Step (5)
12 Scum (5)
13 Flood (5)
14 Stray (3)
15 Bar (5)
17 Dwell (5)
18 Deal (5)
20 Stayed (8)
22 Ballad (3)
25 Pen (5)
26 Laud (5)
28 Tart (4)
29 Cease (4)
30 Break (4)
32 Enemy (3)

Evening Standard ════

191

ACROSS

4 Untrue (5)
7 Animal (6)
9 Aged (3)
10 Hill (3)
12 Bordered (5)
13 Temper (4)
15 Revolt (5)
17 Coma (6)
19 Every (4)
20 Vision (5)
22 Youth (3)
24 Also (7)
27 Sister (3)
28 Shabby (5)
31 Roster (4)
33 Dared (6)
35 View (5)
37 Murder (4)
38 Share (5)
39 Solidify (3)
41 Moose (3)
42 Ebb (6)
43 Gem (5)

DOWN

1. Moulded (6)
2. Relegate (6)
3. Heated (3)
4. Abscond (4)
5. Confuse (5)
6. Drew (8)
8. Ripped (4)
11. Resting (9)
14. Dingy (4)
16. Globule (4)
18. So be it (4)
21. Steadfast (8)
23. Lectern (4)
25. Certain (4)
26. Search (4)
29. Revised (6)
30. Shouted (6)
32. Flower (5)
34. Prophet (4)
36. Visit (4)
40. Limb (3)

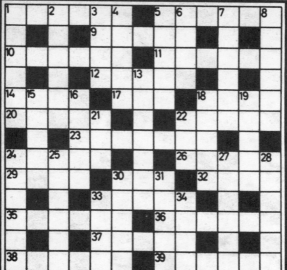

192

ACROSS

1 Doorway (6)
5 Shrewdness (6)
9 Throw (5)
10 Decayed (6)
11 Followed (6)
12 Dissuade (5)
14 Tender (4)

DOWN

1 Read (6)
2 Withdraw (6)
3 Imitated (4)
4 Wrinkled (5)
5 Performed (5)
6 Scorch (4)
7 Thawed (6)

17 Performed (3)
18 Present (4)
20 Occurrence (5)
22 Paddled (5)
23 Twisted (7)
24 Command (5)
26 Cap (5)
29 Agitate (4)

8 Elbowed (6)
13 Thrilled (7)
15 Open (5)
16 Go in (5)
18 Hell (5)
19 Spree (5)
21 Sailor (3)
22 Network (3)
24 Stableman (6)

30 Encountered (3)
32 Only (4)
33 Died away (5)
35 Clear (6)
36 Element (6)
37 Beer (5)
38 Save (6)
39 See-saw (6)

25 Obscured (6)
27 Firework (6)
28 Cashier (6)
30 Title (5)
31 Principle (5)
33 Rasp (4)
34 Dreadful (4)

Evening Standard ═══

193

ACROSS

3 Condition (5)
9 Guide (6)
10 Amatory (6)
11 Irrigate (5)
12 Candid (4)
15 Cultivate (4)
17 Ran (7)
20 Regret (3)
21 Sovereign (5)
23 Fastened (4)
25 Wound (4)
26 Twelve (5)
28 Whim (3)
30 News (7)
33 Holly (4)
35 Duo (4)
36 Suspect (5)
38 Atelier (6)
39 Vessel (6)
40 Verdant (5)

DOWN

1 Melancholy (5)
2 Harbour (5)
3 Stitch (3)
4 Dealer (6)
5 Pour (4)
6 Stray (3)
7 Step (5)
8 Climb (5)
13 Incomplete (7)
14 Called (5)
16 Baggage (7)
18 Quilt (5)
19 Chop (3)
22 Inflexible (5)
24 Cur (3)
27 Agile (6)
28 Initial (5)
29 Outcoming (5)
31 Elbow (5)
32 Begin (5)
34 Entrance (4)
36 Delve (3)
37 Cask (3)

194

ACROSS

1 Oppose (6)
5 Consider (4)
8 Quietened (5)
9 Observe (3)
10 Tidy (4)
11 Quote (4)
12 Guide (5)

DOWN

1 Haunt (6)
2 First-class (8)
3 Transgressed (6)
4 Disfigured (9)
5 Deciphered (7)
6 Revise (4)

13 Assistance (6)
16 Facts (4)
18 Discharge (4)
20 Finish (3)
22 Drunkard (3)
23 Barrier (3)
24 Fury (4)
25 Over-sweet (4)
28 Soak (6)

7 Encounter (4)
8 Chart (3)
14 Tying (9)
15 Obscure (3)
17 Pull (3)
19 Attractive (8)
20 Spike (3)
21 Ordained (7)
26 Worn (6)

30 Stadium (5)
32 Sugar lump (4)
33 Frozen (4)
34 Gratuity (3)
35 Inclined (5)
36 Watched (4)
37 Elicited (6)

27 Moulded (6)
29 Pain (4)
30 Competent (4)
31 Deed (3)

Evening Standard

195

ACROSS

1 Fold (5)
5 Disperse (6)
8 Pigs (5)
10 Immoral (6)
11 Heroic (4)
14 Dedicate (6)
15 Compete (7)

18 Colour (3)
19 Consume (3)
21 Repose (4)
23 Change (5)
24 Unite (4)
27 Still (3)
29 Fish (3)
31 Discouraged (7)

32 Meal (6)
34 Season (4)
35 Harmony (6)
38 Advantage (5)
39 Totter (6)
40 Tired (5)

DOWN

2 Meadow (3)
3 Shrewd (6)
4 Pair (3)
5 Act (4)
6 Slice (6)
7 Hidden (6)
9 Stupidly (7)

12 Through (3)
13 Cipher (4)
16 Formerly (4)
17 Old-fashioned (5)
20 Lockjaw (7)
22 Sensible (4)
24 Jammed (6)
25 Loaned (4)

26 Refuted (6)
28 Ask (6)
30 Guided (3)
33 Breed (4)
36 Novel (3)
37 Scull (3)

196

ACROSS

2 Upright (5)
7 Stump (4)
8 Spoil (6)
9 Beast (5)
11 Performed (3)
13 Free (3)
15 Paradise (4)

16 Drink delicately (3)
18 Sport (4)
19 Attacked (7)
20 Part (4)
22 Rubbish-tip (4)
23 Moment (7)
25 Transmit (4)

27 Moose (3)
28 Gala (4)
30 Observe (3)
31 Defective (3)
33 Droll (5)
36 Picture-house (6)
37 One (4)
38 Aristocratic (5)

DOWN

1 Sober (5)
2 Recede (3)
3 Bird (3)
4 Fasten (3)
5 Fitting (3)
6 Shinbone (5)
10 Threesome (4)

11 Dishearten (7)
12 Refuse (7)
13 Diminished (7)
14 Fell (7)
16 Condition (5)
17 Trick (5)
18 Marry (3)
21 Finish (3)
24 Too (4)

26 Weird (5)
29 Jacket (5)
32 Fixed (3)
33 Tin (3)
34 Crowd (3)
35 Hint (3)

Evening Standard

ACROSS

2 Enquired (5)
7 Orb (5)
8 Worship (5)
10 Use (5)
12 Wonder (3)
13 Rasp (5)
15 Fell (7)
17 Venerate (6)
19 Damp (3)
20 Penetrated (7)
23 Stated (4)
25 Dreadful (4)
26 Liberate (7)
30 Resin (3)
31 Determine (6)
34 Abraded (7)
37 Quoted (5)
38 Plaything (3)
39 Stupefied (5)
40 Cringe (5)
41 Demise (5)
42 Guide (5)

DOWN

1 Blaze (5)
2 Diminish (5)
3 Strict (6)
4 Discharge (4)
5 Adjusted (7)
6 Salute (5)
9 Bird (3)
11 Reduced (7)
13 Clutch (5)
14 Evade (5)
16 Through (3)
18 Lured (7)
21 Number (5)
22 Stitched (5)
24 Hindered (7)
27 Circuit (3)
28 Ebb (6)
29 Performer (5)
32 Drink (5)
33 God (5)
35 Rank (3)
36 Dash (4)

198

ACROSS

1 Broad (4)
4 Mire (3)
6 Ceremony (4)
8 Cheerful (6)
9 Greedily (6)
10 Label (3)
12 Marine growth (5)
14 Lukewarm (5)
15 Yielded (5)
18 Sofa (6)
20 Fruit (6)
24 Famous (5)
26 Sprig (5)
28 Suspect (5)
30 Away (3)
32 Offer (6)
33 Revert (6)
34 Employed (4)
35 Ballad (3)
36 Sketched (4)

DOWN

2 Ice-house (5)
3 Take out (7)
4 Encounter (4)
5 Haul (4)
6 Elevate (5)
7 Effective (7)
11 Imitate (3)
12 Lettuce (3)
13 Shelter (3)
16 Lair (3)
17 Spot (3)
19 State (7)
21 Blushing (3)
22 Assumed (7)
23 Newt (3)
25 Lout (3)
27 Helped (5)
29 Canal-boat (5)
30 Spoken (4)
31 Conflict (4)

Evening Standard

199

ACROSS

1 Annul (6)
5 Die (6)
8 Sham (8)
9 Subside (4)
10 Border (3)
12 Coffer (5)
15 Permit (3)
17 Tree (3)
18 Sheep (3)
19 Tavern (3)
20 Likeness (5)
21 Everything (3)
22 Wrath (3)
23 Brown (3)
24 Beverage (3)
26 New (5)
29 Attempt (3)
33 Pain (4)
34 Explode (8)
35 Promise (6)
36 Tyrant (6)

DOWN

2 Concur (5)
3 Quote (4)
4 Meal (5)
5 Iron (5)
6 Hazard (4)
7 Because (5)
10 Raise (5)
11 Madness (5)
12 Principal (5)
13 Delete (5)
14 Cogs (5)
15 Inclined (5)
16 Agree (5)
25 Surpass (5)
27 Crest (5)
28 Located (5)
30 Proportion (5)
31 Repair (4)
32 Responsibility (4)

200

ACROSS

1 Image (4)
4 Skill (3)
6 Stuff (4)
9 Moo (3)
10 Perplexed (8)
11 Cheese (4)
14 Plus (3)
16 Avarice (5)
19 Abandoned (8)
21 Alloy (5)
23 Claimed (8)
24 Sum (5)
27 Tease (3)
31 Footwear (4)
33 Novel (8)
34 Stray (3)
35 Worry (4)
36 Cur (3)
37 Consider (4)

DOWN

2 Entrance (4)
3 Raise (4)
4 Agreed (8)
5 Neat (4)
6 Transparent (5)
7 Wand (3)
8 Not asleep (5)
12 Confess (5)
13 Advantage (5)
14 Limb (3)
15 Dissuade (5)
17 Escape (5)
18 Fop (5)
20 Injurious (8)
22 Loiter (3)
25 Alternative (5)
26 Deflect (5)
28 Frigid (4)
29 Object (4)
30 Decline (4)
32 Mineral (3)

Evening Standard

201

ACROSS

4 Booth (5)
7 Haunt (6)
9 Transgress (3)
10 Lettuce (3)
12 Flourished (5)
13 Timber (4)
15 Lac (5)
17 Regret (6)
19 Discharge (4)
20 Inn (5)
22 Drink (3)
24 Ebbed (7)
27 Sicken (3)
28 Respond (5)
31 Sketched (4)
33 Tried (6)
35 Fat (5)
37 Finished (4)
38 Sordid (5)
39 Weaken (3)
41 Epoch (3)
42 Gift (6)
43 Inclined (5)

DOWN

1 Increase (6)
2 Accompany (6)
3 Curve (3)
4 Bird (4)
5 Silly (5)
6 Particular (8)
8 Ripped (4)
11 Foolish (9)
14 Caribou (4)
16 Fastener (4)
18 Excuse (4)
21 Supervisor (8)
23 Saucy (4)
25 Quote (4)
26 Act (4)
29 Worshipped (6)
30 Agreement (6)
32 Females (5)
34 Chair (4)
36 Cowshed (4)
40 Wages (3)

202

ACROSS

1 Stubborn (6)
5 Beetle (6)
9 Attain (5)
10 Fruit (6)
11 Attacker (6)
12 Senior (5)
14 Story (4)
17 Pull (3)
18 Lake (4)
20 Occurrence (5)
22 Fruit (5)
23 Turned (7)
24 Guide (5)
26 Implicit (5)
29 Image (4)
30 Stitch (3)
32 Thoroughfare (4)
33 Enciphered (5)
35 Dog-house (6)
36 Immersed (6)
37 Lament (5)
38 Evaded (6)
39 Reviser (6)

DOWN

1 Discussion (6)
2 Mild (6)
3 Sea-eagle (4)
4 Traded (5)
5 Twist (5)
6 Scorch (4)
7 Recover (6)
8 Sterile (6)
13 Gave (7)
15 Shun (5)
16 Enlist (5)
18 Decoration (5)
19 Bird (5)
21 Child (3)
22 Permit (3)
24 Chosen (6)
25 Lent (6)
27 Floor-covering (6)
28 Offer (6)
30 Compact (5)
31 Jam (5)
33 Yield (4)
34 Expired (4)

Evening Standard

203

ACROSS

3 Garret (5)
9 Withdraw (6)
10 Hurried (6)
11 Singer (5)
12 Wicked (4)
15 Step (4)
17 Diminished (7)
20 Because (3)
21 Stream (5)
23 Flat (4)
25 Essence (4)
26 Old-fashioned (5)
28 Fuel (3)
30 Loss (7)
33 Formerly (4)
35 Sand-hill (4)
36 Restrict (5)
38 Shoe (6)
39 Inherent (6)
40 Twelve (5)

DOWN

1 Command (5)
2 Sober (5)
3 Skill (3)
4 See-saw (6)
5 Press (4)
6 Dog (3)
7 Bundle (5)
8 Viper (5)
13 Old campaigner (7)
14 Enticed (5)
16 Include (7)
18 Plunged (5)
19 Fix (3)
22 Inflexible (5)
24 Horse (3)
27 Delineate (6)
28 Furze (5)
29 View (5)
31 Eros (5)
32 Principle (5)
34 Grain-store (4)
36 Youth (3)
37 Brown (3)

204

ACROSS

1 Flaw (6)
5 Daybreak (4)
8 Staid (5)
9 Silent (3)
10 Stigma (4)
11 Raise (4)
12 Implant (5)
13 Cashier (6)
16 Bird (4)
18 Paradise (4)
20 Vehicle (3)
22 Rug (3)
23 Obscure (3)
24 Naked (4)
25 Imitated (4)
28 Allay (6)
30 Intended (5)
32 Peruse (4)
33 Fate (4)
34 Tease (3)
35 Dissuade (5)
36 Pip (4)
37 Free-flowing (6)

DOWN

1 Relegate (6)
2 Intimate (8)
3 Pamper (6)
4 Tortured (9)
5 Erased (7)
6 Parched (4)
7 Observe (4)
8 Prosecute (3)
14 Rest (9)
15 Border (3)
17 Knock (3)
19 Scatter (8)
20 Tin (3)
21 Ebbed (7)
26 Dreary (6)
27 Escape (6)
29 Cupid (4)
30 Forced (4)
31 Hill (3)

Evening Standard

205

ACROSS

1 Lariat (5)
5 Drooped (6)
8 Stadium (5)
10 Purloined (6)
11 Whip (4)
14 Reveal (6)
15 Frightened (7)

DOWN

2 Fitting (3)
3 Wages (6)
4 Mineral (3)
5 Auction (4)
6 Panted (6)
7 Rely (6)
9 Bore (7)

18 Fish (3)
19 Butt (3)
21 Deceased (4)
23 Leaf (5)
24 Liability (4)
27 Lair (3)
29 Help (3)
31 Congregated (7)

12 Hatchet (3)
13 Cavity (4)
16 Comfort (4)
17 Afterwards (5)
20 Ran (7)
22 Summit (4)
24 Wreckage (6)
25 Poet (4)
26 Wearisome (6)

32 Hand-cart (6)
34 Eat (4)
35 Ran off (6)
38 Loaded (5)
39 Snub (6)
40 Bordered (5)

28 Nut (6)
30 Fellow (3)
33 Seam (4)
36 Shelter (3)
37 Watch (3)

206

ACROSS

2 Command (5)
7 Quarrel (4)
8 Aft (6)
9 Passionate (5)
11 Obscure (3)
13 Barrier (3)

15 Cheese (4)
16 Border (3)
18 Nip (4)
19 Boring (7)
20 Stuff (4)
22 Stupefy (4)
23 Vessel (7)
25 Want (4)
27 Scull (3)

28 Grain-husks (4)
30 Performed (3)
31 Large (3)
33 Muzzle (5)
36 Ebb (6)
37 Detail (4)
38 Jam (5)

DOWN

1 Inflexible (5)
2 Away (3)
3 Owing (3)
4 Beam (3)
5 Pig-pen (3)
6 Handle (5)
10 Regretted (4)

11 Fall (7)
12 Ran (7)
13 Agitate (7)
14 Import (7)
16 Greeting (5)
17 Lesser (5)
18 Coach (3)
21 Insane (3)
24 Deserve (4)

26 Sea-duck (5)
29 Pointed (5)
32 Damp (3)
33 Stitch (3)
34 Aged (3)
35 Fasten (3)

Evening Standard

207

ACROSS

2 Brittle (5)
7 Kind (5)
8 Object (5)
10 Go in (5)
12 Feline (3)
13 Cap (5)
15 Deserved (7)
17 Staggered (6)
19 Youth (3)
20 Swelled (7)
23 Pip (4)
25 Expensive (4)
26 Lived (7)
30 Evil (3)
31 Wish (6)
34 Rotted (7)
37 Renowned (5)
38 Tankard (3)
39 Slept (5)
40 Drain (5)
41 Change (5)
42 Trivial (5)

DOWN

1 Quay (5)
2 Fishing-basket (5)
3 Hired (6)
4 Staunch (4)
5 Determined (7)
6 Quietened (5)
9 Rug (3)
11 Eased (7)
13 Bumptious (5)
14 Allude (5)
16 Rodent (3)
18 Parted (7)
21 Material (5)
22 Generate (5)
24 Discussed (7)
27 State (3)
28 Beat (6)
29 Repulse (5)
32 Sorrowfully (5)
33 Revolt (5)
35 Intimidate (3)
36 Finished (4)

208

ACROSS

1 Centre (4)
4 Beaker (3)
6 Sort (4)
8 View (6)
9 Vent (6)
10 Owned (3)
12 Purloin (5)

14 Bar (5)
15 Short (5)
18 Maintain (6)
20 Deserved (6)
24 Dig (5)
26 Scoff (5)
28 Finished (5)
30 Marry (3)

32 Forthcoming (6)
33 Recompense (6)
34 Revise (4)
35 Cur (3)
36 Obligation (4)

DOWN

2 Start (5)
3 Raise (7)
4 Legend (4)
5 Righteous (4)
6 Name (5)
7 Lead (7)
11 Donkey (3)

12 Ocean (3)
13 Limb (3)
16 Colour (3)
17 Fish (3)
19 Listless (7)
21 Greeting (3)
22 Renovated (7)
23 Defective (3)
25 Stretch (3)

27 Burst (5)
29 Heron (5)
30 Join (4)
31 Haul (4)

Evening Standard

209

ACROSS

1 Proper (6)
5 Character (6)
8 Ate (8)
9 Absent (4)
10 Fixed (3)
12 Viper (5)
15 Permit (3)

17 Mat (3)
18 Employ (3)
19 Spring (3)
20 Praise (5)
21 Vehicle (3)
22 Males (3)
23 Watch (3)
24 Circuit (3)
26 Weary (5)

29 Untruth (3)
33 Abrupt (4)
34 Awful (8)
35 Custodian (6)
36 Sanctify (6)

DOWN

2 Arouse (5)
3 Comfort (4)
4 Domesticated (5)
5 Deposit (5)
6 Side (4)
7 Delete (5)

10 Fibre (5)
11 Hobo (5)
12 Representative (5)
13 Dissuade (5)
14 Reigned (5)
15 Flat (5)
16 Taut (5)
25 Sharp (5)

27 Bury (5)
28 Soil (5)
30 Ice-house (5)
31 Cease (4)
32 Cultivate (4)

210

ACROSS

1 Spoken (4)
4 Enclosure (3)
6 Ribbon (4)
9 Epoch (3)
10 View (8)
11 Skin-trouble (4)

14 Obese (3)
16 Respond (5)
19 Obtained (8)
21 Singer (5)
23 Objected (8)
24 Exclude (5)
27 Can (3)
31 Network (4)
33 Original (8)

34 Mineral (3)
35 Reared (4)
36 Regret (3)
37 Pull (4)

DOWN

2 Unusual (4)
3 Final (4)
4 Ready (8)
5 Observe (4)
6 Torment (5)
7 Curve (3)
8 Confusion (5)

12 Rescued (5)
13 Firework (5)
14 Suitable (3)
15 Principle (5)
17 Worship (5)
18 Commerce (5)
20 Home (8)
22 Manage (3)
25 Mistake (5)

26 Appended (5)
28 Box (4)
29 Remain (4)
30 Soon (4)
32 Wrath (3)

Evening Standard

211

ACROSS

4 Initial (5)
7 Rampaged (6)
9 Enthusiast (3)
10 Evil (3)
12 Silly (5)
13 Pace (4)
15 Name (5)

DOWN

1 Emergency (6)
2 Precede (6)
3 Network (3)
4 Lose (4)
5 Interior (5)
6 Unique (8)
8 Facts (4)

17 Fat (6)
19 Vanquish (4)
20 Endured (5)
22 Snoop (3)
24 Slandered (7)
27 And not (3)
28 Memorise (5)
31 Prima donna (4)

11 Decry (9)
14 Poke (4)
16 Period (4)
18 Paradise (4)
21 Smarten (8)
23 Shout (4)
25 Bird (4)
26 Caribou (4)
29 Nuclear (6)

33 Note case (6)
35 Protuberance (5)
37 Part (4)
38 Claw (5)
39 Consume (3)
41 Vigour (3)
42 Beginner (6)
43 Cap (5)

30 Wanted (6)
32 Over (5)
34 Thin (4)
36 One (4)
40 Summit (3)

212

ACROSS

1 Niche (6)
5 Slumbering (6)
9 Month (5)
10 Mess (6)
11 Centre (6)
12 Domesticated (5)
14 Auction (4)
17 Free (3)
18 Speed (4)
20 Vapour (5)
22 Cabled (5)
23 Twisted (7)
24 Skinflint (5)
26 Liability (5)
29 Image (4)
30 Cot (3)
32 Discourteous (4)
33 Pattern (5)
35 Cause (6)
36 Sloth (6)
37 Postpone (5)
38 Staggered (6)
39 Peruser (6)

DOWN

1 Careless (6)
2 Pamper (6)
3 Sailor (4)
4 Javelin (5)
5 Pointed (5)
6 Slipped (4)
7 Charm (6)
8 Stripped (6)
13 Mixed (7)
15 Garret (5)
16 Consumed (5)
18 Jockey (5)
19 Lukewarm (5)
21 Spoil (3)
22 Marry (3)
24 Reflect (6)
25 Comfort (6)
27 Jolted (6)
28 Dread (6)
30 Filleted (5)
31 Dissuade (5)
33 Method (4)
34 Learning (4)

Evening Standard

213

ACROSS

3 Forbidden (5)
9 Epistle (6)
10 Sterile (6)
11 Performer (5)
12 Imitated (4)
15 Formerly (4)
17 Wed (7)
20 Deity (3)
21 Swift (5)
23 Expensive (4)
25 Bearing (4)
26 Stirred (5)
28 Limb (3)
30 Guard (7)
33 Image (4)
35 Roster (4)
36 Sham (5)
38 Embraced (6)
39 Venerate (6)
40 Principle (5)

DOWN

1 Glimmer (5)
2 Guide (5)
3 Beverage (3)
4 Bowman (6)
5 Instrument (4)
6 Scull (3)
7 Fetch (5)
8 Finished (5)
13 Waded (7)
14 Vision (5)
16 Join (7)
18 Old-fashioned (5)
19 Obscure (3)
22 Eater (5)
24 Steal (3)
27 Modest (6)
28 Supple (5)
29 Ravine (5)
31 Famous (5)
32 Relaxed (5)
34 Travelled (4)
36 Wager (3)
37 Fixed (3)

214

ACROSS

1 Bear (6)
5 Search (4)
8 Drain (5)
9 Ban (3)
10 Ale (4)
11 Fever (4)
12 Stroll (5)

13 Peril (6)
16 Denomination (4)
18 Leader (4)
20 Guided (3)
22 Child (3)
23 Yelp (3)
24 Team (4)
25 Employed (4)

28 Flower (6)
30 Carried (5)
32 Intelligence (4)
33 Measure (4)
34 Fish (3)
35 Demon (5)
36 Clump (4)
37 Revised (6)

DOWN

1 Incorporate (6)
2 Maddened (8)
3 Hydrophobia (6)
4 Allowed (9)
5 Sound (7)

6 Impel (4)
7 Pour (4)
8 Ocean (3)
14 Reverting (9)
15 Faucet (3)
17 Lettuce (3)
19 Soonest (8)
20 Illuminated (3)
21 Lodge (7)

26 Darted (6)
27 Pale (6)
29 Unite (4)
30 Polish (4)
31 Finish (3)

Evening Standard

215

ACROSS

1 Jumped (5)
5 Filter (6)
8 Spree (5)
10 Delineate (6)
11 Press (4)
14 Obvious (6)
15 Brief (7)

18 Vegetable (3)
19 Tavern (3)
21 Cart (4)
23 Engine (5)
24 Cot (4)
27 Entrap (3)
29 Age (3)
31 Sifted (7)
32 Stared (6)

34 Too (4)
35 Team (6)
38 Loaded (5)
39 Breakwater (6)
40 Map-book (5)

DOWN

2 Stretch (3)
3 Royal son (6)
4 Number (3)
5 Mistake (4)
6 Deeply-
  planted (6)
7 Tidily (6)

9 Interpretation
  (7)
12 Knock (3)
13 Close (4)
16 Finished (4)
17 Go in (5)
20 Observed (7)
22 Competent (4)
24 Managing (6)

25 Thought (4)
26 Grain (6)
28 Coming (6)
30 Aye (3)
33 Distribute (4)
36 Meadow (3)
37 Epoch (3)

216

ACROSS

2 Explode (5)
7 Loyal (4)
8 Source (6)
9 Entice (5)
11 Tin (3)
13 Free (3)
15 Cheese (4)

16 Edge (3)
18 Dandy (4)
19 Flew (7)
20 Ripped (4)
22 Cloudy (4)
23 Versus (7)
25 Singer (4)
27 Owing (3)
28 Dread (4)

30 Untruth (3)
31 Performed (3)
33 Feeling (5)
36 Opportunity (6)
37 Recognised (4)
38 Brief (5)

DOWN

1 Wide (5)
2 Wager (3)
3 Butt (3)
4 Child (3)
5 Delve (3)
6 Shinbone (5)
10 Bucket (4)

11 Middle (7)
12 Recount (7)
13 Diminished (7)
14 Dunce (7)
16 Inflexible (5)
17 Code (5)
18 Cot (3)
21 Self (3)
24 Naked (4)

26 Supple (5)
29 Helped (5)
32 Finish (3)
33 Fixed (3)
34 And not (3)
35 Stretch (3)

Evening Standard

217

ACROSS

2 Worship (5)
7 Gaze (5)
8 Lawful (5)
10 Tender (5)
12 Bed (3)
13 Near (5)
15 Determined (7)
17 Disclose (6)
19 Sever (3)
20 Taught (7)
23 Additional (4)
25 Expensive (4)
26 Entwined (7)
30 Ocean (3)
31 Fame (6)
34 Beleaguer (7)
37 Quoted (5)
38 Regret (3)
39 Praise (5)
40 Birds (5)
41 Liability (5)
42 War-horse (5)

DOWN

1 Purloined (5)
2 Ascended (5)
3 Beat (6)
4 Rush (4)
5 Read out (7)
6 Loathed (5)
9 Deity (3)
11 Regain (7)
13 Felony (5)
14 Open (5)
16 Dog (3)
18 Baggage (7)
21 Outcoming (5)
22 Avarice (5)
24 Simplest (7)
27 Born (3)
28 Decipher (6)
29 Cap (5)
32 Heaped (5)
33 Lukewarm (5)
35 Prosecute (3)
36 Way out (4)

218

ACROSS

1 Remit (4)
4 Conflict (3)
6 Cried (4)
8 Gaol (6)
9 Manner (6)
10 Faucet (3)
12 Spate (5)

14 Stableman (5)
15 Beleaguer (5)
18 Gift (6)
20 Emanated (6)
24 Sail-boat (5)
26 Handle (5)
28 Cede (5)
30 Beer (3)
32 Recover (6)

33 Item (6)
34 Curve (4)
35 Rabbit (3)
36 Near (4)

DOWN

2 Enlist (5)
3 Undress (7)
4 Require (4)
5 Incline (4)
6 Irrigate (5)
7 Incite (7)

11 Wonderment (3)
12 Obese (3)
13 Lair (3)
16 Pig-pen (3)
17 Twitch (3)
19 Accomplish (7)
21 Timid (3)

22 Cheese (7)
23 Father (3)
25 Sicken (3)
27 Liberated (5)
29 Mendacious (5)
30 Between (4)
31 Rim (4)

Evening Standard

219

ACROSS

1 Disappear (6)
5 Safe (6)
8 Demean (8)
9 Discourteous (4)
10 Feline (3)
12 Incline (5)
15 Drunkard (3)
17 Skill (3)
18 Spout (3)
19 Lubricate (3)
20 Living (5)
21 Mineral (3)
22 Scull (3)
23 Vehicle (3)
24 Knowledge (3)
26 Taut (5)
29 Consume (3)
33 Certain (4)
34 Sunk (8)
35 Promise (6)
36 Hostility (6)

DOWN

2 Stadium (5)
3 Flag (4)
4 Inn (5)
5 Slumber (5)
6 Centre (4)
7 Wireless (5)
10 Timepiece (5)
11 Claw (5)
12 Begin (5)
13 Due (5)
14 Evict (5)
15 Stock (5)
16 Handle (5)
25 Equivalent (5)
27 Emanate (5)
28 Dwelling (5)
30 Deflect (5)
31 Guide (4)
32 Staunch (4)

220

ACROSS

1 Elderly (4)
4 Intimidate (3)
6 Too (4)
9 Immerse (3)
10 Persuade (8)
11 Detail (4)
14 Help (3)

16 Fortunate (5)
19 Kept (8)
21 Repulse (5)
23 Gift (8)
24 Alarm (5)
27 Summit (3)
31 Ponder (4)
33 Handcuffed (8)

34 Beverage (3)
35 Sense (4)
36 Fasten (3)
37 Title (4)

DOWN

2 Increase (4)
3 Plunge (4)
4 Restricted (8)
5 Cry (4)
6 Goodbye (5)
7 Illuminated (3)
8 Utter (5)

12 Crawl (5)
13 Blemish (5)
14 Tune (3)
15 Storehouse (5)
17 Courteous (5)
18 Youthful (5)
20 Condemn (8)
22 Circuit (3)
25 Sharp (5)

26 Perfect (5)
28 Soot particle (4)
29 Scrutinise (4)
30 Side (4)
32 Observe (3)

Evening Standard

221

ACROSS

4 Heathen (5)
7 Voucher (6)
9 Border (3)
10 Marry (3)
12 Attain (5)
13 Excuse (4)
15 Lac (5)

17 Ready (6)
19 Soil (4)
20 Consumed (5)
22 Butt (3)
24 Maintained (7)
27 Aye (3)
28 Nude (5)
31 Minus (4)
33 Promise (6)

35 Board (5)
37 Rip (4)
38 Unbend (5)
39 Barrier (3)
41 Colour (3)
42 Pale (6)
43 War-horse (5)

DOWN

1 Principal (6)
2 Take (6)
3 Novel (3)
4 Fairy (4)
5 Correct (5)
6 Precise (8)
8 Period (4)

11 Disheartened (9)
14 Region (4)
16 Deer (4)
18 Sole (4)
21 Follower (8)
23 Food-list (4)
25 Thin (4)
26 Dash (4)

29 Eagerly (6)
30 Scorn (6)
32 Scanty (5)
34 Smack (4)
36 Cut (4)
40 Rug (3)

222

ACROSS

1 Amuse (6)
5 Subtract (6)
9 Lubricated (5)
10 Carnival (6)
11 Individual (6)
12 Fire-raising (5)
14 Dregs (4)
17 Deed (3)
18 Only (4)
20 Finished (5)
22 Engine (5)
23 Waster (7)
24 Renovate (5)
26 Shy (5)
29 Parched (4)
30 Spout (3)
32 Gamble (4)
33 Seraglio (5)
35 Embraced (6)
36 Sickness (6)
37 Allude (5)
38 Staggered (6)
39 Nursed (6)

DOWN

1 Pollute (6)
2 Swerved (6)
3 Roster (4)
4 Head-dress (5)
5 Storehouse (5)
6 Paradise (4)
7 Result (6)
8 Itinerant (6)
13 Strew (7)
15 Go in (5)
16 Stitched (5)
18 Compact (5)
19 Reasoning (5)
21 Bird (3)
22 Encountered (3)
24 Sooner (6)
25 Fuss (6)
27 Overlooked (6)
28 Claim (6)
30 Exhausted (5)
31 Principle (5)
33 Present (4)
34 Horse (4)

Evening Standard

223

ACROSS

3 Irrigate (5)
9 Rota (6)
10 Bulk (6)
11 Generate (5)
12 Tart (4)
15 Fume (4)
17 Flood (7)
20 Fate (3)
21 Entice (5)
23 Amphibian (4)
25 Excursion (4)
26 Confusion (5)
28 Donkey (3)
30 Given (7)
33 Employed (4)
35 Tardy (4)
36 Dance (5)
38 Advantageous (6)
39 Climb (6)
40 Cabin (5)

DOWN

1 Handle (5)
2 Moving (5)
3 Network (3)
4 Rank (6)
5 Always (4)
6 Wand (3)
7 Rustic (5)
8 Cap (5)
13 Admit (7)
14 Sag (5)
16 Epicure (7)
18 Lukewarm (5)
19 Fitting (3)
22 Sum (5)
24 Breach (3)
27 Fight (6)
28 Presage (5)
29 Drain (5)
31 Domesticated (5)
32 Demise (5)
34 Govern (4)
36 Massage (3)
37 Tree (3)

224

ACROSS

1 Diminish (6)
5 Moist (4)
8 Pick-me-up (5)
9 Lettuce (3)
10 Caribou (4)
11 Vessel (4)
12 Concur (5)
13 Cashier (6)
16 Departed (4)
18 Scrutinise (4)
20 Viper (3)
22 Favourite (3)
23 Fish (3)
24 Rank (4)
25 Pitcher (4)
28 Tended (6)
30 Chosen (5)
32 Atmosphere (4)
33 Soon (4)
34 Regret (3)
35 Endure (5)
36 Leg-joint (4)
37 Span (6)

DOWN

1 Relate (6)
2 Reveal (8)
3 Club (6)
4 Overlooked (9)
5 Illness (7)
6 Pain (4)
7 Conduit (4)
8 Beverage (3)
14 Contrite (9)
15 Friend (3)
17 Not many (3)
19 Blamed (8)
20 Sicken (3)
21 Bishop (7)
26 Athlete (6)
27 Stick (6)
29 Reservoir (4)
30 Gaelic (4)
31 Finish (3)

Evening Standard

Answers

PUZZLE No. 1. Across: 4, Hardy. 7, Reader. 9, Mob. 10, Top. 12, Lasso. 13, Lump. 15, Beset. 17, Arrest. 19, Earl. 20, Canoe. 22, Tan. 24, Wagered. 27, Par. 28, Erase. 31, Diva. 33, Tinder. 35, Scene. 37, Wrap. 38, Quota. 39, Gap. 41, Elk. 42, Runner. 43, Pearl. **Down:** 1, Frolic. 2, Layman. 3, Set. 4, Hole. 5, Abate. 6, Distress. 8, Robe. 11, Pestering. 14, Prow. 16, Star. 18, Reap. 21, Altitude. 23, Need. 25, Gate. 26, Drew. 29, Arrant. 30, Expire. 32, Aster. 34, Near. 36, Call. 40, Pup.

PUZZLE No. 2. Across: 1, Loiter. 5, Butted. 9, Widen. 10, Toiled. 11, Giving. 12, Remit. 14, Arch. 17, Ran. 18, Ague. 20, Loyal. 22, Fiend. 23, Decreed. 24, Cared. 26, Denim. 29, Onus. 30, Men. 32, Dude. 33, Kudos. 35, Outfit. 36, Tumble. 37, Lever. 38, Ascend. 39, Defray. **Down:** 1, Lethal. 2, Idiocy. 3, Ewer. 4, Rider. 5, Begin. 6, Unit. 7, Twinge. 8, Dogged. 13, Married. 15, Rowan. 16, Hades. 18, Aided. 19, Undid. 21, Led. 22, Fed. 24, Corona. 25, Rustic. 27, Number. 28, Merely. 30, Muted. 31, Noted. 33, Kiln. 34, Sure.

PUZZLE No. 3. Across: 3, Gloss. 9, Coffee. 10, Etched. 11, Tally. 12, Leer. 15, Fear. 17, Enraged. 20, Tie. 21, Robot. 23, Avid. 25, Grim. 26, Dated. 28, Ace. 30, Descend. 33, Melt. 35, Kite. 36 Below. 38, Sector. 39, Defeat. 40, Beret. **Down:** 1, Scale. 2, Offer. 3, Get. 4, Leader. 5, Sell. 6, Sty. 7, Sheet. 8, Adore. 13, Enhance. 14, Rapid. 16, Ailment. 18, Dozed. 19, Log. 22, Trick. 24, Day. 27, Decode. 28, Amuse. 29, Elect. 31, Eider. 32, Deity. 34, Mere. 36, Bob. 37, Wet.

PUZZLE No. 4. Across: 1, Quarry. 5, Damp. 8, Sleep. 9, Inn. 10, Plea. 11, Feat. 12, Ached. 13, Earned. 16, Dire. 18, Chit. 20, Car. 22, Son. 23, Eat. 24, Sale. 25, Teem. 28, Dispel. 30, Genre. 32, Bear. 33, Bend. 34, Net. 35, Level. 36, Eyed. 37, Mended. **Down:** 1, Quiver. 2, Abnormal. 3, Ripped. 4, Slackened. 5, Defence. 6, Aped. 7, Pity. 8, Sea. 14, Disturbed. 15, Pit. 17, Roe. 19, Happened. 20, Can. 21, Revered. 26, Middle. 27, Elated. 29, Able. 30, Gale. 31, Eel

PUZZLE No. 5: 1, Gusto. 5, Direct. 8, Adieu. 10, Seeped. 11, Male. 14, Pledge. 15, General. 18, End. 19, Lad. 21, Type. 23, Alter. 24, Slid. 27, Yen. 29, Did. 31, Risible. 32, Plover. 34, Line. 35, Entire. 38, Annul. 39, Ragged. 40, Berth. **Down:** 2, Use. 3, Tapped. 4, Ode. 5, Dump. 6, Relent. 7, Thieve. 9, Ideally. 12, Ale. 13, Eddy. 16, Evil. 17, Later. 20, Denizen. 22, Poll. 24, Supper. 25, Idol. 26, Diving. 28, Little. 30, Den. 33, Read. 36, Nub. 37, Rut.

PUZZLE No. 6. Across: 2, Water. 7, Shoe. 8, Asleep. 9, Tarry. 11, Asp. 13, Red. 15, Belt. 16, Map. 18, Sale. 19, Deleted. 20, Long. 22, Till. 23, Turning. 25, Seen. 27, Toy. 28, Part. 30, Hid. 31, Lie. 33, Fared. 36, Recede. 37, Urge. 38, Dated. **Down:** 1, Chose. 2, Wet. 3, Tor. 4, Ray. 5, Old. 6, Revel. 10, Real. 11, Abolish. 12, Planted. 13, Radical. 14, Deflate. 16, Meant. 17, Penny. 18, Set. 21, Gun. 24, Iota. 26, Eider. 29, Ridge. 32, Men. 33, Fed. 34, Rut. 35, Dud.

PUZZLE No. 7. Across: 2, Cease. 7, Learn. 8, Below. 10, Adore. 12, Rat. 13, Stove. 15, Enticed. 17, Thread. 19, Rod. 20, Related. 23, Over. 25, Dent. 26, Replied. 30, Sea. 31, Demise. 34, Prepare. 37, Voter. 38, Ore. 39, Error. 40, Slack. 41, Taken. 42, Level. **Down:** 1, Teeth. 2, Crave. 3, Endear. 4, Sore. 5, Derided. 6, Hotel. 9, Lac. 11, Enraged. 13, Stood. 14, Order. 16, Tot. 18, Declare. 21, Debit. 22, Steer. 24, Respect. 27, Pea. 28, Devote. 29, Droll. 32, Moral. 33, Sewer. 35, Era. 36, Erse.

PUZZLE No. 8. Across: 1, Grip. **4,** Fad. **6,** Open. **8,** Cleric. **9,** Confer. **10,** Elk. **12,** Arena. **14,** Trend. **15,** Elope. **18,** Stared. **20,** Girdle. **24,** Dogma. **26,** Pivot. **28,** Plant. **30,** Led. **32,** Divine. **33,** Aviary. **34,** Flag. **35,** Fan. **36,** Drew. **Down: 2,** Ruler. **3,** Partner. **4,** Face. **5,** Dock. **6,** Owner. **7,** Eternal. **11,** Lap. **12,** Ass. **13,** Ale. **16,** Odd. **17,** Egg. **19,** Trivial. **21,** Imp. **22,** Rallied. **23,** Eft. **25,** Ode. **27,** Owing. **29,** Nerve. **30,** Leaf. **31,** Dawn.

PUZZLE No. 9. Across: 1, Called. **5,** Breach. **8,** Gracious. **9,** Rare. **10,** Per. **12,** Glass. **15,** Sot. **17,** Err. **18,** Tap. **19,** Aim. **20,** Evade. **21,** Urn. **22,** Ire. **23,** Air. **24,** Nut. **26,** Dream. **29,** Nor. **33,** Fund. **34,** Consider **35,** Player. **36,** Yelled. **Down: 2,** Agree. **3,** Luck. **4,** Drool. **5,** Basis. **6,** Earl. **7,** Cargo. **10,** Plain. **11,** Remit. **12,** Greed. **13,** Amaze. **14,** Steam. **15,** Spurn. **16,** Tenor. **25,** Usual. **27,** Recur. **28,** Annoy. **30,** Obese. **31,** Eddy. **32,** Bill.

PUZZLE No. 10. Across: 1, Stop. **4,** Cup. **6,** Cost. **9,** Owl. **10,** Applause. **11,** Unit. **14,** Rip. **16,** Shred. **19,** Captious. **21,** Dunce. **23,** Scrawled. **24,** Delay. **27,** Hat. **31,** Boat. **33,** Reporter. **34,** Die. **35,** Held. **36,** God. **37,** Dare. **Down: 2,** Type. **3,** Pale. **4,** Cautious. **5,** Peer. **6,** Couch. **7,** Own. **8,** Slide. **12,** Acrid. **13,** Appal. **14,** Rid. **15,** Punch. **17,** Reply. **18,** Dowdy. **20,** Scrapped. **22,** Eat. **25,** Erode. **26,** Acted. **28,** Brag. **29,** Trod. **30,** Seer. **32,** Ail

PUZZLE No. 11. Across: 4, Skill. **7,** Recoup. **9,** Gun. **10,** Per. **12,** Round. **13,** Dare. **15,** Renew. **17,** Arrive. **19,** Nous. **20,** Taboo. **22,** Eat. **24,** Spartan. **27,** Eke. **28,** Miser. **31,** Long. **33,** Insect. **35,** Lance. **37,** East. **38,** Debar. **39,** Ear. **41,** Did. **42,** Talent. **43,** Glued. **Down: 1,** Credit. **2,** Scarab. **3,** Cup. **4,** Sure. **5,** Known. **6,** Language. **8,** Peri. **11,** Reverence. **14,** Eros. **16,** Neat. **18,** Rope. **21,** Arboreal. **23,** Tame. **25,** Akin. **26,** Nice. **29,** Stated. **30,** Rotate. **32,** Glade. **34,** Seat. **36,** Arid. **40,** Ray

PUZZLE No. 12. Across: 1, Intact. **5,** Clutch. **9,** Revue. **10,** Pardon. **11,** Barren. **12,** Women. **14,** Lead. **17,** Rid. **18,** Jape. **20,** Eater. **22,** Rated. **23,** Matured. **24,** Depot. **26,** Decay. **29,** Eden. **30,** Web. **32,** Dale. **33,** Hades. **35,** Mallet. **36,** Nickel. **37,** React. **38,** Dodder. **39,** Heated. **Down: 1,** Impale. **2,** Threat. **3,** Crow. **4,** Tenor. **5,** Cubed. **6,** Lean. **7,** Throat. **8,** Handed. **13,** Misused. **15,** Eased. **16,** Demon. **18,** Jaded. **19,** Pedal. **21,** Rat. **22,** Red. **24,** Deemed. **25,** Peeled. **27,** Casket. **28,** Yelled. **30,** Water. **31,** Bench. **33,** Here. **34,** Site

PUZZLE No. 13. Across: 3, Admit. **9,** Armada. **10,** Dither. **11,** Droop. **12,** Idle. **15,** Lack. **17,** Telling. **20,** Foe. **21,** Grate **23,** Itch. **25,** Earl. **26,** Token. **28,** Pet. **30,** Decency. **33,** Idea. **35,** Rate. **36,** Outdo. **38,** Unsure. **39,** Endear. **40,** Blade. **Down: 1,** Habit. **2,** Small. **3,** Add. **4,** Daring. **5,** Idol. **6,** Tip. **7,** Sheaf. **8,** Broke. **13,** Devised. **14,** Elect. **16,** Collect. **18,** Greed. **19,** Ate. **22,** Eager. **24,** Hot. **27,** Needed. **28,** Pique. **29,** Tease. **31,** Named. **32,** Yearn. **34,** Duel. **36,** Orb. **37,** One

PUZZLE No. 14. Across: 1, Resist. **5,** Spar. **8,** Cover. **9,** Gnu. **10,** Room. **11,** Void. **12,** Speed. **13,** Robust. **16,** Safe. **18,** Edam. **20,** Wed. **22,** Net. **23,** Den. **24,** Wide. **25,** Teem. **28,** Devote. **30,** Dealt. **32,** Root. **33,** Iota. **34,** Mar. **35,** Messy. **36,** Bred. **37,** Tender. **Down: 1,** Regard. **2,** Stumbled. **3,** Stress. **4,** Completed. **5,** Severed. **6,** Prod. **7,** Rude. **8,** Cos. **14,** Tantalise. **15,** Man. **17,** Fee. **19,** Deformed. **20,** Wit. **21,** Deleted. **26,** Menace. **27,** Terror. **29,** Grab. **30,** Dome. **31,** Toy

PUZZLE No. 15. Across: 1, Plead. **5,** Appear. **8,** Civic. **10,** Salami. **11,** Harm. **14,** Ensign. **15,** Deficit. **18,** Ton. **19,** Tap. **21,** Need. **23,** Cocoa. **24,** Chic. **27,** Rip. **29,** Rob. **31,** Tuition. **32,** Fooled. **34,** Note. **35,** Abrupt. **38,** Erred. **39,** Roared. **40,** Dying. **Down: 2,** Lea. **3,** Acacia. **4,** Dim. **5,** Ache. **6,** Parson. **7,** Ruined. **9,** Visitor. **12,** Ant. **13,** Mine. **16,** Each. **17,** Tacit. **20,** Popular. **22,** Ergo. **24,** Coffer. **25,** Iron. **26,** Colour. **28,** Sturdy. **30,** Bet. **33,** Deed. **36,** Bed. **37,** Pen

PUZZLE No. 16. Across: 2, Light. 7, True. 8, Ornate. 9, Doubt. 11, Cap. 13, Cog. 15, Onus. 16, Peg. 18, Pale. 19, Barrier. 20, Tide. 22, Post. 23, Instant. 25, Send. 27, Eft. 28, Isle. 30, Tag. 31, Eel. 33, Front. 36, Statue. 37, Over. 38, Deter. **Down:** 1, Organ. 2, Led. 3, Gnu. 4, Tot. 5, Inn. 6, Stool. 10, Beer. 11, Contest. 12, Pudding. 13, Carouse. 14, Genteel. 16, Paste. 17, Grant. 18, Pep. 21, End. 24, Afar. 26, Earth. 29, Level. 32, Ate. 33, Fed. 34, Out. 35, Tor

PUZZLE No. 17. Across: 2, Gaudy. 7, Child. 8, Owner. 10, Ahead. 12, Air. 13, Trade. 15, Defiled. 17, Revere. 19, Fit. 20, Entered. 23, Stir. 25, Dean. 26, Defunct. 30, Car. 31, Easter. 34, Stilted. 37, Style. 38, Emu. 39, Ditto. 40, Lapse. 41, Erred. 42, Shade. **Down:** 1, Share. 2, Glade. 3, Adhere. 4, Dead. 5, Awaited. 6, Beret. 9, Nil. 11, Defence. 13, Trust. 14, Avoid. 16, Fir. 18, Endured. 21, Deity. 22, Inure. 24, Recluse. 27, Fat. 28, Tasted. 29, Stead. 32, Store. 33, Elder. 35, Imp. 36, Dish

PUZZLE No. 18. Across: 1, Stem. 4, Hem. 6, Arch. 8, Wander. 9, Latent. 10, Doe 12, Rapid. 14, Actor. 15, Rider. 18, Parade. 20, United. 24, Noted. 26, Shame. 28, Weary. 30, Yes. 32, Trance. 33, Pallid. 34, Eddy. 35, Lid. 36, Yank. **Down:** 2, Tiara. 3, Madeira. 4, Hard. 5, Male. 6, Attic. 7, Console. 11, Ode. 12, Rip. 13, Did. 16, Den. 17, Rut. 19, Adhered. 21, New. 22, Ideally. 23, Dry. 25, Ore. 27, Money. 29, Reign. 30, Yell. 31, Sped

PUZZLE No. 19. Across: 1, Astute. 5, Tragic. 8, Recently. 9, Leap. 10, Spa. 12, Taste. 15, Sew. 17, Per. 18, Nip. 19, Nap. 20, Exact. 21, Ear. 22, Lea. 23, Era. 24, Eye. 26, Donor. 29, Key. 33, Vain. 34, Saturate. 35, Intent. 36, Result. **Down:** 2, Steep. 3, Used. 4, Extra. 5, Tryst. 6, Able. 7, Irate. 10, Since. 11, Apple. 12, Tread. 13, Stain. 14, Enter. 15, Speak. 16, Worry. 25, Yearn. 27, Onset. 28, Outer. 30, Extol. 31, Once. 32, Kris

PUZZLE No. 20. Across: 1, Stop. 4, Sip. 6, Step. 9, Pen. 10, Constant. 11, Earl. 14, Met. 16, Adult. 19, Declared. 21, Tenor. 23, Demolish. 24, Dread. 27, Tit. 31, Mule. 33, Emanated. 34, Sin 35, Seed 36, Due 37, Told. **Down:** 2, Tool. 3, Pest. 4, Slavered. 5, Pity. 6, Spend. 7, Tea. 8, Enrol. 12, Edged. 13, Score. 14, Mat. 15, Tenet. 17, Undid. 18, Tight. 20, Dominate. 22, Rot. 25, Rouse. 26, Amend. 28, Feed 29, Cant. 30, Meal. 32, Lie

PUZZLE No. 21. Across: 4, Canal. 7, Roused. 9, Log. 10, Pup. 12, Arson. 13, Teem. 15, Crate. 17, Doctor. 19, Edam. 20, Spoor. 22, Vim. 24, Decided. 27, Wad. 28, Erect. 31, Fume. 33, Rested. 35, Scene. 37, Will. 38, Lasso. 39, Tap. 41, Air. 42, Morose. 43, Beryl. **Down:** 1, Gratis. 2, Tuxedo. 3, Pep. 4, Coat. 5, Agree. 6, Aromatic. 8, Duct. 11, Provident. 14, Mood. 16, Arid. 18, Crew. 21, Populace. 23, Meet. 25, Care. 26, Drew. 29, Editor. 30, Teller. 32, Essay. 34, Seam. 36, Coil. 40, Pod

PUZZLE No. 22. Across: 1, Beaker. 5, Bottom. 9, Wider. 10, Helped. 11, Ration. 12, Revel. 14, Stew. 17, Rat. 18, Oval. 20, Topic. 22, Sieve. 23, Radical. 24, Sewed. 26, Tepid. 29, Prod. 30, Tug. 32, Dude. 33, Basic. 35, Ordeal. 36, Vulgar. 37, Rover. 38, Tureen. 39, Needle. **Down:** 1, Behest. 2, Asleep. 3, Ewer. 4, Rider. 5, Beret. 6, Oral. 7, Thieve. 8, Mangle. 13, Various. 15, Tower. 16, Wired. 18, Oiled. 19, Avoid. 21, Cad. 22, Sat. 24, Sprout. 25, Wonder. 27, Purged. 28, Decree. 30, Talon. 31, Given. 33, Bare. 34, Cure.

PUZZLE No. 23. Across: 3, Waver. 9, Rolled. 10, Sodden. 11, Drape. 12, Mien. 15, Nice. 17, Amnesia. 20, Tar. 21, Tired. 23, Aped. 25, Test. 26, Ruler. 28, Set. 30, Deserve. 33, Edit. 35, Reel. 36, Aided. 38, Enrage. 39, Dulcet. 40, Edged. **Down:** 1, Drama. 2, Alien. 3, Wed. 4, Adroit. 5, Espy. 6, Roe. 7, Admit. 8, Under. 13, Impaled. 14, Never. 16, Captive. 18, Aimed. 19, Pet. 22, Deter. 24, Due. 27, Recede. 28, Sewer. 29, Tiara. 31, Reach. 32, Elite. 34, Died. 36, Age. 37, Dud.

PUZZLE No. 24. Across: 1, Direct. **5,** Dark. **8,** Sober. **9,** Rim. **10,** Seer. **11,** Scan. **12,** Epoch. **13,** Driver. **16,** Tear. **18,** Norm. **20,** Per. **22,** Ice. **23,** Try. **24,** Tide. **25,** Neat. **28,** Lizard. **30,** Depot. **32,** Read. **33,** Road. **34,** Ire. **35,** React. **36,** Bred. **37,** Ardent. **Down: 1,** Deride. **2,** Remained. **3,** Cosset. **4,** Corporeal. **5,** Descent. **6,** Arch. **7,** Kind. **8,** See. **14,** Reinforce. **15,** Pry. **17,** Ace. **19,** Organise. **20,** Pit. **21,** Receded. **26,** Tinder. **27,** Advent. **29,** Grab. **30,** Dare. **31,** Tot.

PUZZLE No. 25. Across: 1, Chief. **5,** Basked. **8,** Villa. **10,** Adhere. **11,** Role. **14,** Dredge. **15,** Mislead. **18,** End. **19,** Lob. **21,** Type. **23,** Alley. **24,** Axed. **27,** Yen. **29,** Dim. **31,** Delight. **32,** Clever. **34,** Nine. **35,** Idiocy. **38,** Noted. **39,** Detest. **40,** Needy. **Down: 2,** Hid. **3,** Evenly. **4,** Fir. **5,** Bard. **6,** Silent. **7,** Delete. **9,** Legally. **12,** Ore. **13,** Eddy. **16,** Ibex. **17,** Doled. **20,** Benefit. **22,** Path. **24,** Accord. **25,** Eden. **26,** Divine. **28,** Divide. **30,** Men. **33,** Rent. **36,** Den. **37,** Cod.

PUZZLE No. 26. Across: 2, Sense. **7,** Ache. **8,** Expose. **9,** Appal. **11,** Car. **13,** Red. **15,** Apex. **16,** Per. **18,** Late. **19,** Denoted. **20,** Aver. **22,** Till. **23,** Dubious. **25,** Eden. **27,** Lie. **28,** Part. **30,** Rid. **31,** Lee. **33,** Eyrie. **36,** Cinema. **37,** Raid. **38,** Rider. **Down: 1,** Scrap. **2,** Sea. **3,** Nip. **4,** Eel. **5,** Ape. **6,** Asset. **10,** Amen. **11,** Cadaver. **12,** Receded. **13,** Radical. **14,** Deplete. **16,** Peril. **17,** Rogue. **18,** Let. **21,** Run. **24,** Oily. **26,** Digit. **29,** Remit. **32,** Set. **33,** Ear. **34,** Rod. **35,** Err.

PUZZLE No. 27. Across: 2, Daunt. **7,** Rapid. **8,** Valid. **10,** Noted. **12,** Nil. **13,** Cower. **15,** Debated. **17,** Reader. **19,** Fig. **20,** Decided. **23,** Tied. **25,** Drum. **26,** Retired. **30,** Van. **31,** Daring. **34,** Floored. **37,** Genie. **38,** Eat. **39,** Dodge. **40,** Beret. **41,** Educe. **42,** Glory. **Down: 1,** Canoe. **2,** Dined. **3,** Adored. **4,** Need. **5,** Managed. **6,** Piled. **9,** Lit. **11,** Defiled. **13,** Crate. **14,** Water. **16,** Bid. **18,** Refined. **21,** Drain. **22,** Image. **24,** Devoted. **27,** Tar. **28,** Dagger. **29,** Sleep. **32,** Reedy. **33,** Niece. **35,** Oar. **36,** Doll.

PUZZLE No. 28. Across: 1, Diva. **4,** Rub. **6,** Sick. **8,** Closed. **9,** Called. **10,** Elk. **12,** Money. **14,** Learn. **15,** Regal. **18,** Delete. **20,** Orator. **24,** Total. **26,** Spoil. **28,** Macaw. **30,** Sly. **32,** Ravage. **33,** Ermine. **34,** Once. **35,** Tap. **36,** Dolt. **Down: 2,** Igloo. **3,** Austere. **4,** Ride. **5,** Back. **6,** Salve. **7,** Cheerio. **11,** Lea. **12,** Mad. **13,** Yet. **16,** Get. **17,** Lot. **19,** Explain. **21,** Ram. **22,** Alarmed. **23,** Raw. **25,** Oil. **27,** Irate. **29,** Annul. **30,** Seat. **31,** Yelp.

PUZZLE No. 29. Across: 1, Absent. **5,** Defeat. **8,** Material. **9,** Lost. **10,** Wet. **12,** Refer. **15,** End. **17,** Ire. **18,** Aim. **19,** Era. **20,** Idiot. **21,** Bar. **22,** Rug. **23,** Eye. **24,** Pea. **26,** Naked. **29,** Rue. **33,** Fine. **34,** Terrific. **35,** Pester. **36,** Runner. **Down: 2,** Blame. **3,** Even. **4,** Trite. **5,** Delve. **6,** Fell. **7,** Arson. **10,** Whelp. **11,** Tiara. **12,** Reign. **13,** Frisk. **14,** Rated. **15,** Ember. **16,** Dirge. **25,** Elite. **27,** Alter. **28,** Error. **30,** Unite. **31,** Heat. **32,** Mien.

PUZZLE No. 30. Across: 1, Stem. **4,** Dog. **6,** Task. **9,** All. **10,** Collapse. **11,** Bear. **14,** Act. **16,** Level. **19,** Inventor. **21,** Tenet. **23,** Diminish. **24,** Lodge. **27,** Cap. **31,** Wife. **33,** Lukewarm. **34,** Vie. **35,** Herd. **36,** Bad. **37,** Bane. **Down: 2,** Tool. **3,** Male. **4,** Depicted. **5,** Glee. **6,** Table. **7,** Ale. **8,** Slake. **12,** Vital. **13,** Avoid. **14,** Ant. **15,** Tonic. **17,** Visit. **18,** Lithe. **20,** Remarked. **22,** Tip. **25,** Olive. **26,** Greed. **28,** Club. **29,** Swab. **30,** Iron. **32,** Fir.

PUZZLE No. 31. Across: 4, Shape. **7,** Rocket. **9,** Sea. **10,** Tee. **12,** Error. **13,** Teem. **15,** Slope. **17,** Debtor. **19,** Mood. **20,** Scene. **22,** Nap. **24,** Dangled. **27,** Tea. **28,** Ready. **31,** Pass. **33,** Stated. **35,** Miser. **37,** Roll. **38,** Duvet. **39,** Dim. **41,** Leg. **42,** Delete. **43,** Realm. **Down: 1,** Gratis. **2,** Accede. **3,** Wet. **4,** Seep. **5,** Harem. **6,** Promoted. **8,** Test. **11,** Elongated. **14,** Mend. **16,** Oral. **18,** Beat. **21,** Creature. **23,** Pert. **25,** Ness. **26,** Deer. **29,** Adored. **30,** Yelled. **32,** Smell. **34,** Arid. **36,** Item. **40,** Men.

PUZZLE No. 32. Across: 1, Indeed. **5**, Reared. **9**, Valid. **10**, Timber. **11**, Gifted. **12**, Remit. **14**, Clad. **17**, Did. **18**, Cede. **20**, Tenet. **22**, Fared. **23**, Burglar. **24**, Robin. **26**, Tenor. **29**, Unit. **30**, Wed. **32**, Dune. **33**, Hades. **35**, Notion. **36**, Cobble. **37**, Legal. **38**, Ranted. **39**, Yearly. **Down: 1**, Intact. **2**, Demean. **3**, Ever. **4**, Dared. **5**, Rigid. **6**, Edit. **7**, Rather. **8**, Dodged. **13**, Mingled. **15**, Lemon. **16**, Debit. **18**, Cared. **19**, Demon. **21**, Tun. **22**, Fat. **24**, Runner. **25**, Bitten. **27**, Number. **28**, Remedy. **30**, Waned. **31**, Decay. **33**, Hole. **34**, Sole.

PUZZLE No. 33. Across: 3, Wedge. **9**, Rotted. **10**, Ravine. **11**, Eider. **12**, Evil. **15**, Wise. **17**, Donated. **20**, Act. **21**, Dined. **23**, Crew. **25**, Tell. **26**, Refer. **28**, Set. **30**, Resumed. **33**, Area. **35**, Tide. **36**, Comic. **38**, Cuckoo. **39**, Subtle. **40**, Spite. **Down: 1**, Breed. **2**, Stain. **3**, Wee. **4**, Edited. **5**, Grew. **6**, Ear. **7**, Tibia. **8**, Beset. **13**, Voucher. **14**, Later. **16**, Scolded. **18**, Diver. **19**, Get. **22**, Debut. **24**, Web. **27**, Resist. **28**, Sauce. **29**, Teach. **31**, Misty. **32**, Deter. **34**, Coop. **36**, Cos. **37**, Cue.

PUZZLE No. 34. Across: 1, Apiece. **5**, Anon. **8**, Fence. **9**, Tot. **10**, Ewer. **11**, Came. **12**, Ether. **13**,Turnip. **16**, Tern. **18**, Emit. **20**, Bad. **22**, Sue. **23**, Dud. **24**, Male. **25**, Tent. **28**, Tended. **30**, Mould. **32**, Clot. **33**, East. **34**, Roe. **35**, Penny. **36**, Deed. **37**, Bridge. **Down: 1**, Astute. **2**, Internal. **3**, Credit. **4**, Pertinent. **5**, Acceded. **6**, Near. **7**, Need. **8**, Fee. **14**, Pestilent. **15**, Lid **17**, Rue. **19**, Murdered. **20**, Bay. **21**, Demoted. **26**, Tester. **27**, Adhere. **29**, Acid. **30**, Mope. **31**, Day.

PUZZLE No. 35. Across: 1, Clasp. **5**, Gaping. **8**, Eager. **10**, Berate. **11**, Iron. **14**, Divide. **15**, Colonel. **18**, Pen. **19**, Rid. **21**, Defy. **23**, Famed. **24**, Read. **27**, Lip. **29**, Vim. **31**, Torture. **32**, Clever. **34**, Rite **35**, Earthy. **38**, Nudge. **39**, Digest. **40**, Edged. **Down: 2**, Lie. **3**, Season. **4**, Pat. **5**, Grid. **6**, Proved. **7**, Gaiety. **9**, General. **12**, Rip. **13**, Nine. **16**, Once. **17**, Limit. **20**, Deposed. **22**, Fear. **24**, Record. **25**, Aver. **26**, Divine. **28**, Stored. **30**, Met. **33**, Rent. **36**, Age. **37**, Hue.

PUZZLE No. 36. Across: 2, Extol. **7**, Stab. **8**, Astute. **9**, Board. **11**, Dud. **13**, Hod. **15**, Item. **16**, Top. **18**, Pile. **19**, Noticed. **20**, Pier. **22**, Reap. **23**, Tangled. **25**, Teem. **27**, Hid. **28**, Turn. **30**, End. **31**, Sad. **33**, Sever. **36**, Debase. **37**, Unit. **38**, Wince. **Down: 1**, Stout. **2**, Ebb. **3**, Tea. **4**, Lad. **5**, Sty. **6**, Stool. **10**, Root. **11**, Dispute. **12**, Deleted. **13**, Hideous. **14**, Despond. **16**, Tough. **17**, Pined. **18**, Per. **21**, Ram. **24**, Like. **26**, Enter. **29**, Rabid. **32**, Wan. **33**, Sew. **34**, Van. **35**, Rue.

PUZZLE No. 37. Across: 2, State. **7**, Radio. **8**, Fiend. **10**, Tired. **12**, Lag. **13**, Model. **15**, Demoted. **17**, Eroded. **19**, Fat. **20**, Drained. **23**, Need. **25**, Dear. **26**, Debated. **30**, Rim. **31**, Delete. **34**, Created. **37**, Cared. **38**, Ran. **39**, Remit. **40**, Merge. **41**, Dense. **42**, Steer. **Down: 1**, Major. **2**, Sited. **3**, Toiled. **4**, Tied. **5**, Piloted. **6**, Anger. **9**, Eat. **11**, Defiled. **13**, Meant. **14**, Doped. **16**, Man. **18**, Dreamer. **21**, Deter. **22**, Greed. **24**, Derange. **27**, Bit. **28**, Decide. **29**, Erred. **32**, Later. **33**, Tense. **35**, Ear. **36**, Deft

PUZZLE No. 38. Across: 1, Chic. **4**, Dog. **6**, Paid. **8**, Fiance. **9**, Intact. **10**, Dip. **12**, Stood. **14**, Close. **15**, Lined. **18**, Allege. **20**, Inform. **24**, Wider. **26**, Sneer. **28**, Tenet. **30**, Ale. **32**, Buying. **33**, Rigour. **34**, Idle. **35**, Due. **36**, Tier. **Down: 2**, Hoist. **3**, Console. **4**, Deed. **5**, Grip. **6**, Petal. **7**, Incisor. **11**, Ire. **12**, Spa. **13**, Dig. **16**, New. **17**, Did. **19**, Languid. **21**, Net. **22**, Freight. **23**, Mat. **25**, Ill. **27**, Elite. **29**, Exude. **30**, Aged. **31**, Erne.

PUZZLE No. 39. Across: 1, Barren. **5**, Strain. **8**, Tenderly. **9**, Tear. **10**, Bar. **12**, Beset. **15**, Set. **17**, Oil. **18**, Roe. **19**, Ray. **20**, Erase. **21**, Ace. **22**, Ass. **23**, Aim. **24**, Eel. **26**, Steed. **29**, Yet. **33**, Used. **34**, Moderate. **35**, Addled. **36**, Demean. **Down: 2**, Arena. **3**, Ride. **4**, Nerve. **5**, Style. **6**, Rite. **7**, Irate. **10**, Barge. **11**, Royal. **12**, Bless. **13**, Shape. **14**, Tread. **15**, Seamy. **16**, Treat. **25**, Eased. **27**, Tamed. **28**, Ended. **30**, Extra. **31**, Idol. **32**, Grim.

PUZZLE No. 40. Across: 1, Fall. 4, Cup. 6, Rash. 9, Ail. 10, Distance. 11, Idea. 14, Mud. 16, Leapt. 19, Deceased. 21, Refer. 23, Denuding. 24, Trend. 27, Rot. 31, Rude. 33, Convince. 34, Sod. 35, Deny. 36, Die. 37, Lees. **Down:** 2, Avid. 3, Late. 4, Confused. 5, Peer. 6, Raise. 7, Aid. 8, Sleep. 12, Admit. 13, Scene. 14, Mar. 15, Defer. 17, Attic. 18, Tinge. 20, Denounce. 22, Rut. 25, Rouse. 26, Needy. 28, Acid. 29, Kill. 30, Ache. 32, Don.

PUZZLE No. 41. Across: 4, Stump. 7, Raider. 9, For. 10, Top. 12, Lasso. 13, Tomb. 15, Besom. 17, Arrest. 19, Play. 20, Canoe. 22, Tip. 24, Wavered. 27, Par. 28, Rover. 31, Taxi. 33, Little. 35, Scene. 37, Erne. 38, Villa. 39, Gap. 41, Era. 42, Refuse. 43, Unite. **Down:** 1, Erotic. 2, Airman. 3, Set. 4, Solo. 5, Tramp. 6, Massacre. 8, Robe. 11, Pestering. 14, Brow. 16, Stir. 18, Reap. 21, Alsatian. 23, Pert. 25, Vale. 26, Dole. 29, Versus. 30, Reeled. 32, Islet. 34, Tear. 36, Care. 40, Pen.

PUZZLE No. 42. Across: 1, Regard. 5, Slight. 9, Eerie. 10, System. 11, Nation. 12, Doped. 14, Ever. 17, New. 18, Here. 20, Rider. 22, Model. 23, Cartoon. 24, Stout. 26, Beset. 29, Pair. 30, Lid. 32, Dire. 33, Sonic. 35, United. 36, Nipped. 37, Egret. 38, Engine. 39, Defend. **Down:** 1, Roster. 2, Gasped. 3, Reed. 4, Demon. 5, Sinew. 6, Lead. 7, Gained. 8, Tunnel. 13, Pertain. 15, Vista. 16, Recur. 18, Honed. 19, Refer. 21, Rat. 22, Mob. 24, Spruce. 25, Oiling. 27, Simple. 28, Tended. 30, Lodge. 31 Dined. 33, Seen. 34, Cite.

PUZZLE No. 43. Across: 3, Final. 9, Awaken. 10, Vanish. 11, Ethic. 12, Iris. 15, Mine. 17, Descent. 20, Cot. 21, Dated. 23, Part. 25, Peri. 26, Eaten. 28, Ant. 30, Damaged. 33, Idol. 35, Ride. 36, Rigid. 38, Entail. 39, Vendor. 40, Dozen. **Down:** 1, Rapid. 2, Basis. 3, Fee. 4, Intend. 5, Avid. 6, Lac. 7, Civic. 8, Sheet. 13, Respond. 14, Scare. 16, Noticed. 18, Tamed. 19, Rep. 22, Debar. 24, Tan. 27, Native. 28, Aided. 29, Tooth. 31, Giddy. 32, Decry. 34, Silo. 36, Rid. 37, Den.

PUZZLE No. 44. Across: 1, Scrape. 5, Deft. 8, Aimed. 9, Cos. 10, Loss. 11, Feel. 12, Stain. 13, Render. 16, Tern. 18, Emit. 20, Wed. 22, Pad. 23, Dip. 24, Wide. 25, Ewer. 28, Dealer. 30, Aorta. 32, Tact. 33, Ache. 34, Nip. 35, Meant. 36, Need. 37, Terror. **Down:** 1, Secure. 2, Resented. 3, Pullet. 4, Distended. 5, Defiled. 6, Eden. 7, Tale. 8, Ass. 14, Repentant. 15, Rip. 17, Raw. 19, Milliner. 20, Wig. 21, Devoted. 26, Recede. 27, Proper. 29, Stun. 30, Acme. 31, Act.

PUZZLE No. 45. Across: 1, Blast. 5, Tablet. 8, Mania. 10, Gazebo. 11, Roar. 14, Nature. 15, Mislead. 18, Red. 19, Did. 21, Neat. 23, River. 24, Exit. 27, Cad. 29, Say. 31, Numeral. 32, Called. 34, Else. 35, Earned. 38, Nudge. 39, Defray. 40, Edged. **Down:** 2, Lea. 3, Smelly. 4, Tab. 5, Tarn. 6, Beaten. 7, Talent. 9, Nomadic. 12, Oar. 13, Rude. 16, Ibex. 17, Divan. 20, Deduced. 22, Area. 24, Exceed. 25, Isle. 26, Taller. 28, Jeered. 30, Yes. 33, Deny. 36, Age. 37, Eye.

PUZZLE No. 46. Across: 2, Chief. 7, Plea. 8, Elicit 9, Tinge. 11, Mat. 13, Die. 15, Anon. 16, Mad. 18, Cram. 19, Retinue. 20, Deer. 22, Tall. 23, Ringlet. 25, Teem. 27, Ear. 28, Sent. 30, End. 33, Stall. 36, Mutual. 37, Aver. 38, Yield. **Down:** 1, Clean. 2, Cat. 3, Inn. 4, Fee. 5, Bid. 6, Tibia. 10, Gnat. 11, Mandate. 12, Towered. 13, Dreaded. 14, Emulate. 16, Merge. 17, Diner. 18, Cut. 21, Rim. 24, Last. 26, Ensue. 29, Noted. 32, Dub. 33, Sly. 34, Ace. 35, Lad.

PUZZLE No. 47. Across: 2, Fresh. 7, Stare. 8, Rival. 10, Acrid. 12, Lag 13, Drama. 15, Demoted. 17, Relent. 19, Sat. 20, Trainer. 23, Owed. 25, Died. 26, Rotated. 30, Net. 31, Defile. 34, Groaned. 37, Ceded. 38, Art. 39, Digit. 40, Steel. 41, Deter. 42, Sewed. **Down:** 1, Store. 2, Frame. 3, Recant. 4, Slid. 5, Piloted. 6, Wager. 9, Vat. 11, Desired. 13, Droop. 14, Alder. 16, Man. 18, Treated. 21, Rigid. 22, Edged. 24, Donated. 27, Ten. 28, Decide. 29, Crate. 32, Feted. 33, Lever. 35, Ore. 36, Dire.

PUZZLE No. 48. Across: 1, Disc. 4, Top. 6, Vain. 8, Tunnel. 9, Abroad. 10, Den. 12, Debit. 14, Remit. 15, North. 18, Meagre. 20, Amused. 24, Demon. 26, Spent. 28, Baton. 30, Gun. 32, Beaker. 33, Ardent. 34, Used. 35, Tie. 36, Dare. **Down:** 2, Inure. 3, Cunning. 4, Told. 5, Plan. 6, Verge. 7, Imagine. 11, Eat. 12, Dim. 13, Tor. 16, Red. 17, Ham. 19, Express. 21, Mob. 22, Unaided. 23, Don. 25, Emu. 27, Naked. 29, Owner. 30, Grit. 31, Name.

PUZZLE No. 49. Across: 1, Adored. 5, Stupid. 8, Instance. 9, Idle. 10, Lee. 12, Smart. 15, God. 17, Nil. 18, Ill. 19, Act. 20, Exact. 21, Ape. 23, Eye. 24, Lid. 24, Tar. 26, Piece. 29, Elm. 33, Ogre. 34, February. 35, Trader. 36, Needed. **Down:** 2, Dense. 3, Rate. 4, Denim. 5, Sheer. 6, Unit. 7, Igloo. 10, Least. 11, Enter. 12, Sleep. 13, Amaze. 14, Title. 15, Glade. 16, Dream. 25, Anger. 27, Infer. 28, Cabin. 30, Large. 31, Lead. 32, Mute.

PUZZLE No. 50. Across: 1, Drip. 4, Dip. 6, Wise. 9, Era. 10, Boastful. 11, Dell. 14, Bar. 16, Refer. 19, Credited. 21, Tenor. 23, Denoting. 24, Dress. 27, Wad. 31, Nice. 33, Pristine. 34, Sue. 35, Need. 36, Din. 37, Mood. **Down:** 2, Riot. 3, Past. 4, Defeated. 5, Pull. 6, Wedge. 7, Ire. 8, Salve. 12, Acted. 13, Tease. 14, Bit. 15, Renew. 17, Frail. 18, Range. 20, Donation. 22, Rod. 25, Raise. 26, Speed. 28, Sped. 29, Stem. 30, Undo. 32, Cue.

PUZZLE No. 51. Across: 4, Treat. 7, Awning. 9, Woe. 10, Dad. 12, Offer. 13, Scum. 15, Lisle. 17, Repast. 19, Rout. 20, False. 22, Sad. 24, Severed. 27, Ran. 28, Eaten. 31, Mass. 33, Staple. 35, Later. 37, Ease. 38, Scoop. 39, Dip. 41, Pet. 42, Delete. 43, Edged. **Down:** 1, Massif. 2, Unfurl. 3, And. 4, Tool. 5, Refer. 6, Adequate. 8, Gala. 11, Dissented. 14, Mess. 16, Star. 18, Peer. 21, Advanced. 23, Deep. 25, Vast. 26, Dale. 29, Teased 30, Needed. 32, Slope. 34, Arid. 36, Aped. 40, Pen.

PUZZLE No. 52. Across: 1, Assume. 5, Clutch. 9, Ensue. 10, Falter. 11, Regret. 12, Tower. 14, Idol. 17, Lad. 18, Fade. 20, Renew. 22, Alter. 23, Vestige. 24, Cased. 26, Eerie. 29, Oral. 30, Inn. 32, Told. 33, Anger. 35, Meagre. 36, Violet. 37, Creep. 38, Slight. 39, Render. **Down:** 1, Affair. 2, Salmon. 3, Meet. 4, Enrol. 5, Cured. 6, Leer. 7, Throat. 8, Hither. 13, Wanting. 15, Debar. 16 Level. 18, Fleet. 19, Devil. 21, Wed. 22, Age. 24, Commis. 25, Salami. 27, Rolled. 28, Editor. 30, Inert. 31, Never. 33, Arch. 34, Ripe.

PUZZLE No. 53. Across: 3, Attic. 9, Repose. 10, Damage. 11, Sleep. 12, Eros. 15, Wise. 17, Defined. 20, Old. 21, Rigid. 23, Item. 25, Prop. 26, Dated. 28, Lea. 30, Divided. 33, Idle. 35, Nude. 36, Rebel. 38, Horrid. 39, Caress. 40, Deity. **Down:** 1, Greed. 2, Spoof. 3, Ass. 4, Teller. 5, Idea. 6, Cap. 7, Radio. 8, Sewed. 13, Retired. 14, Sited. 16, Slapped. 18, Dived. 19, Tip. 22, Drain. 24, Mar. 27, Direct. 28, Lithe. 29, Alert. 31, Duped. 32, Dense. 34, Cede. 36, Rid. 37, Lay.

PUZZLE No. 54. Across: 1, Depart. 5, Seat. 8, Voted. 9, Nee. 10, Grim. 11, Cite. 12, Apart. 13, Hectic. 16, Note. 18, Toil. 20, Sea. 22, Net. 23, Err. 24, Hard. 25, Teem. 28, Docile. 30, Arena. 32, Rule. 33, Unit. 34, Ail. 35, Asset. 36, Boss. 37, Played. **Down:** 1, Dinghy. 2, Preacher. 3, Regain. 4, Completed. 5, Secrete. 6, Edit. 7, Tied. 8, Via. 14, Continued. 15, Fir. 17, Tee. 19, Ordinary. 20, Sap. 21, Address. 26, Mortal. 27, Yelled. 29, Grab. 30, Alas. 31, Ant.

PUZZLE No. 55. Across: 1, Sharp. 5, System. 8, Aisle. 10, Ignite. 11, Edam. 14, Mature. 15, Beneath. 18, Yet. 19, Lid. 21, Debt. 23, Beret. 24, Test. 27, Red. 29, Leg. 31, Duteous. 32, Coined. 34, Data. 35, Enough. 38, Rider. 39, Tattle. 40, Wedge. **Down:** 2, Hog. 3, Raider. 4, Pit. 5, Seem. 6, Seated. 7, Molest. 9, Settler. 12, Day. 13, Mute. 16, Edge. 17, Hired. 20, Deduced. 22, Beau. 24, Ticket. 25, Slid. 26, Tenant. 28, Before. 30, Get. 33, Dare. 36, New. 37, Gag.

PUZZLE No. 56. Across: 2, Dream. 7, Beau. 8, Abacus. 9, Draft. 11, Air. 13, All. 15, Sled. 16, Aid. 18, Bite. 19, Doleful. 20, User. 22, Smug. 23, Auction. 25, Ease. 27, Art. 28, Inch. 30, Die. 31, Toy. 33, Snare. 36, Refine. 37, Knew. 38, Theme. **Down:** 1, Devil. 2, Dud. 3, Era. 4, Mat. 5, Ray. 6, Quilt. 10, Foil. 11, Assured. 12, Release. 13, Ailment. 14, Lengthy. 16, Aorta. 17, Depot. 18, Bus. 21, Rue. 24, Iron. 26, Aimed. 29, Cover. 32, Pit. 33, Set. 34, Awe. 35, Eke.

PUZZLE No. 57. Across: 2, Grasp. 7, Padre. 8, Deter. 10, Ended. 12, Car. 13, Sewed. 15, Desired. 17, Elated. 19, Bed. 20, Relaxed. 23, Seer. 25, Dire. 26, Retired. 30, Pan. 31, Defame. 34, Grouped. 37, Minor. 38, Eat. 39, Donor. 40, Fared. 41, Tease. 42, Greed. **Down:** 1, Label. 2, Greet. 3, Render. 4, Sped. 5, Decided. 6, Beret. 9, Tar. 11, Debated. 13, Sense. 14, Water. 16, Sex. 18, Defined. 21, Divan. 22, Sever. 24, Reputed. 27, Tap. 28, Demote. 29, Great. 32, Fired. 33, Moose. 35, Oar. 36, Door.

PUZZLE No. 58. Across: 1, Taxi. 4, Tag. 6, Oral. 8, Faster. 9, Excite. 10, New. 12, Among. 14, Trick. 15, Seedy. 18, Lovely. 20, Eleven. 24, Eaten. 26, Essay. 28, Tacit. 30, Wed. 32, Depose. 33, Enlist. 34, Mere. 35, Pad. 36, Drew. **Down:** 2, Alarm. 3, Intense. 4, Torn. 5, Grew. 6, Occur. 7, Article. 11, End. 12, Ail. 13, Gel. 16, Eye. 17, Yet. 19, Obscene. 21, Let. 22, Enabled. 23, Net. 25, Ape. 27, Above. 29, Issue. 30, Weep. 31, Dead.

PUZZLE No. 59. Across: 1, Podium. 5, Trance. 8, Mistaken. 9, Unit. 10, Age. 12, Creep. 15, Eft. 17, Duo. 18, Urn. 19, Log. 20, Wager. 21, Elk. 22, Ewe. 23, Gem. 24, Wad. 26, Dirge. 29, Yen. 33, Fine. 34, Paradise. 35, Kennel. 36, Erased. **Down:** 2, Owing. 3, Iota. 4, Maker. 5, Tense. 6, Ague. 7, Chief. 10, Allow. 11, Edged. 12, Cowed. 13, Eager. 14, Purge. 15, Enemy. 16, Token. 25, Alike. 27, Impel. 28, Gorse. 30, Ensue. 31, Seen. 32, Idea.

PUZZLE No. 60. Across: 1, Stem. 4, Sit. 6, Acid. 9, Rod. 10, Diverted. 11, Owed. 14, Bat. 16, Dealt. 19, Operator. 21, Repel. 23, Deserted. 24, Rider. 27, Red. 31, Halt. 33, Revolver. 34, Tee. 35, Beer. 36, Did. 37, Plot. **Down:** 2, Trip. 3, Meet. 4, Situated. 5, Tidy. 6, Arose. 7, Cow. 8, Ideal. 12, Motor. 13, Fetid. 14, Bar. 15, Toper. 17, Acute. 18, Tardy. 20, Reserved. 22, Led. 25, Irate. 26, Enter. 28, Grid. 29, Clap. 30, Zero. 32, Lee.

PUZZLE No. 61: Across: 4, Canal. 7, Affirm. 9, Top. 10, Rep. 12, Match. 13, Prod. 15, Never. 17, Refuse. 19, Test. 20, Deter. 22, Ten. 24, Revered. 27, Ear. 28, Aroma. 31, Area. 33, Sister. 35, Scene. 37, Wail. 38, Lasso. 39, Gem. 41, Era. 42, Mangle. 43, White. **Down:** 1, Gasped. 2, Effort. 3, Err. 4, Come. 5, Apart. 6, Accustom. 8, Menu. 11, Pestering. 14, Deer. 16, Veer. 18, Free. 21, Encroach. 23, Neat. 25, Vase. 26, Drew. 29, Orange. 30, Asleep. 32, Asset. 34, Seem. 36, Core. 40, Mad.

PUZZLE No. 62. Across: 1, Uproar. 5, Corona. 9, Rowan. 10, Idiocy. 11, Rustic. 12, Hades. 14, Ever. 17, Led. 18, Kiln. 20, Dared. 22, Muted. 23, Managed. 24, Rigid. 26, Noted. 29, Edit. 30, Fed. 32, Sure. 33, Aided. 35, Twinge. 36, Number. 37, Undid. 38, Dogged. 39, Merely. **Down:** 1, United. 2, Raider. 3, Arch. 4, Royal. 5, Cared. 6, Onus. 7, Outfit. 8, Ascend. 13, Defaced. 15, Valid. 16, Remit. 18, Kudos. 19, Lever. 21, Dad. 22, Men. 24, Rested. 25, Giving. 27, Tumble. 28, Defray. 30, Fiend. 31, Denim. 33, Ague. 34, Dude.

PUZZLE No. 63. Across: 3, Argue. 9, Morose. 10, Gender. 11, Scull. 12, Ease. 15, Fete. 17, Dispose. 20, Red. 21, Stall. 23, Mice. 25, Dear. 26, Haven. 28, End. 30, Respect. 33, Step. 35, Tier. 36, Study. 38, Azalea. 39, Legend. 40, Aries. **Down:** 1, Embed. 2, Crass. 3, Ass. 4, Recess. 5, Ugly. 6, Eel. 7, Adder. 8, Greed. 13, Ailment. 14, Epoch. 16, Terrace. 18, Ether. 19, Old. 22, Leapt. 24, Eat. 27, Needle. 28, Essay. 29, Debar. 31, Eider. 32, Trade. 34, Star. 36, Sea. 37, Yes.

PUZZLE No. 64. Across: 1, Accede. **5,** Dais. **8,** Sever. **9,** Ire. **10,** Soil. **11,** Vice. **12,** Timid. **13,** Hectic. **16,** Loft. **18,** Edam. **20,** Rod. **22,** Ail. **23,** Did. **24,** Mine. **25,** Grew. **28,** Dangle. **30,** Villa. **32,** Plea. **33,** Avid. **34,** Air. **35,** State. **36,** Note. **37,** Urgent. **Down: 1,** Alight. **2,** Coercion. **3,** Distil. **4,** Belittled. **5,** Devised. **6,** Arid. **7,** Stem. **8,** Sit. **14,** Coagulate. **15,** Sad. **17,** Fir. **19,** Disgrace. **20,** Rip. **21,** Deviate. **26,** Wander. **27,** Regret. **29,** Spin. **30,** Vest. **31,** Ave.

PUZZLE No. 65. Across: 1, Treat. **5,** Lifted. **8,** Badge. **10,** Emerge. **11,** Aped. **14,** Palate. **15,** Despair. **18,** Yet. **19,** Car. **21,** Rest. **23,** Ripen. **24,** Stir. **27,** Tip. **29,** Dab. **31,** Ductile. **32,** Plover. **34,** Lido. **35,** Earned. **38,** Ladle. **39,** Recede. **40,** Edged. **Down: 2,** Rum. **3,** Abrupt. **4,** Tag. **5,** Leap. **6,** Feeler. **7,** Defect. **9,** Deficit. **12,** Pay. **13,** Date. **16,** Emit. **17,** Rapid. **20,** Reputed. **22,** Sell. **24,** Supper. **25,** Idol. **26,** Ravine. **28,** Stored. **30,** Bed. **33,** Role. **36,** Ale. **37,** Eye.

PUZZLE No. 66. Across: 2, Ideal **7,** Evil **8,** Indeed **9,** Leapt. **11,** Rid. **13,** Aid. **15,** Edit. **16,** Big. **18,** Free. **19,** Deliver. **20,** Unit. **22,** Data. **23,** Dilated. **25,** Even. **27,** Nun. **28,** Ague. **30,** Did. **31,** End. **33,** Saved. **36,** Divine. **37,** Emit. **38,** Train. **Down: 1,** Avoid. **2,** Ill. **3,** Era. **4,** Lit. **5,** Add. **6,** Eerie. **10,** Pail. **11,** Refuted. **12,** Divided. **13,** Arrange. **14,** Debated. **16,** Began. **17,** Given. **18,** Fed. **21,** Tin. **24,** Tuna. **26,** Visit. **29,** Undid. **32,** Wit. **33,** Set. **34,** Via. **35,** Den.

PUZZLE No. 67. Across: 2, Abhor. **7,** Tibia. **8,** Mural. **10,** Dream. **12,** Rat. **13,** Sewer. **15,** Learned. **17,** Traded. **19,** Eye. **20,** Distend. **23,** Over. **25,** Trio. **26,** Resting. **30,** Tea. **31,** Garner. **34,** Torrent. **37,** Needy. **38,** Boa. **39,** Twine. **40,** Fetch. **41,** Educe. **42,** Unity. **Down: 1,** Miser. **2,** Aided. **3,** Barred. **4,** Oral. **5,** Current. **6,** Rated. **9,** Ran. **11,** Meeting. **13,** Stool. **14,** Water. **16,** Aye. **18,** Distant. **21,** Drone. **22,** Lorry. **24,** Retract. **27,** See. **28,** Gannet. **29,** Robed. **32,** Reedy. **33,** Edict. **35,** Rot. **36,** Twin.

PUZZLE No. 68. Across: 1 Chic. **4,** Pit. **6,** Back. **8,** Manner. **9,** Nether. **10,** Tag. **12,** Level. **14,** Entry. **15,** React. **18,** Totter. **20,** Orator. **24,** Titan. **26,** Staff. **28,** Widen. **30,** Bed. **32,** Damage. **33,** Abacus. **34,** Yell. **35,** Top. **36,** Ewer. **Down: 2,** Heave **3,** Concert. **4,** Part. **5,** Tang. **6,** Baton. **7,** Cheerio. **11,** Arc. **12,** Lot. **13,** Lee. **16,** Art. **17,** Tot. **19,** Outrage. **21,** Raw. **22,** Animate. **23,** Run. **25,** Ire. **27,** Frail. **29,** Exude. **30,** Beat. **31,** Damp.

PUZZLE No. 69. Across: 1, Sinner. **5,** Wanted. **8,** Returned. **9,** Mate. **10,** Ate. **12,** Sever. **15,** Sac. **17,** Nut. **18,** Eel. **19,** Lad. **20,** Odium. **21,** Emu. **22,**, Err. **23,** Imp. **24,** Sad. **26,** Erect. **29,** Tip. **33,** Fine. **34,** Purchase. **35,** Tunnel. **36,** Eleven. **Down: 2,** Inept. **3,** Nous. **4,** Range. **5,** Wedge. **6,**, Name. **7,** Extra. **10,** Atlas. **11,** Ended. **12,** Store. **13,** Voice. **14,** Remit. **15,** Slept. **16,** Clump. **25,** Adieu. **27,** Repel. **28,** Curse. **30,** Issue. **31,** Mean. **32,** Shoe.

PUZZLE No. 70. Across: 1, Grid. **4,** Cap. **6,** Slap. **9,** Car. **10,** Convince. **11,** Apex. **14,** Bit. **16,** Petal. **19,** Preceded. **21,** Tenor. **23,** Renounce. **24,** Nomad. **27,** Tab. **31,** Once. **33,** Pristine. **34,** Cur. **35,** Meet. **36,** Yen. **37,** Pipe. **Down: 2,** Room. **3,** Dive. **4,** Consider. **5,** Peer. **6,** Scare. **7,** Lap. **8,** Arena. **12,** Spurn. **13,** Realm. **14,** Bet. **15,** Tenet. **17,** Taint. **18,** Lover. **20,** Donation. **22,** Rob. **25,** Ounce. **26,** Avert. **28,** Spry. **29,** Stop. **30,** Snap. **32,** Cue.

PUZZLE No. 71. Across: 4, Pride. **7,** Ironed. **9,** See. **10,** Lac. **12,** Range. **13,** Wood. **15,** Topic. **17,** Urbane. **19,** Heed. **20,** Mural. **22,** Sew. **24,** Bustled. **27,** Ear. **28,** Sidle. **31,** Less. **33,** Filter. **35,** Piece. **37,** Dear. **38,** Aided. **39,** Tap. **41,** Elm. **42,** Decree. **43,** Grade. **Down: 1,** Wigwam. **2,** Colour. **3,** Gel. **4,** Peri. **5,** Reach. **6,** Doggerel. **8,** Data. **11,** Constrict. **14,** Drab. **16,** Peel. **18,** Blue. **21,** Ulterior. **23,** West. **25,** Safe. **26,** Died. **29,** Dreary. **30,** Earned. **32,** Speed. **34,** Lead. **36,** Idle. **40,** Pet.

PUZZLE No. 72. Across: 1, Enmesh. 5, Dented. 9, Oozed. 10, Output. 11, Billed. 12, Rebut. 14, User. 17, Lit. 18, Hole. 20, Strip. 22, Sewer. 23, Delayed. 24, Alter. 26, Agree. 29, Tear. 30, Arm. 32, Earn. 33, Creel. 35, Mentor. 36, Differ. 37, Nomad. 38, Curlew. 39, Lovely. **Down:** 1, Exodus. 2, Matter. 3, Sour. 4, Hotel. 5, Debut. 6, Edit. 7, Tallow. 8, Dodder. 13, Bizarre. 15, Stole. 16, Rider. 18, Hedge. 19, Lever. 21, Per. 22, Sea. 24, Atomic. 25, Tanner. 27, Raffle. 28, Energy. 30, Arrow. 31, Medal. 33, Cone. 34, Lido.

PUZZLE No. 73. Across: 3, Aries. 9, Hearse. 10, Minute. 11, Stain. 12, Slip. 15, Face. 17, Masonry. 20, Lot. 21, Night. 23, Grew. 25, Yawn. 26, Rifle. 28, God. 30, Drained. 33, Oral. 35, Tore. 36, Devil. 38, Sultan. 39, Neater. 40, Duvet. **Down:** 1, Chasm. 2, Basis. 3, Ass. 4, Return. 5, Emit. 6, Sin. 7, Rural. 8, Beret. 13, Languor. 14, Power. 16, Counter. 18, Yield. 19, Shy. 22, Tacit. 24, Wit. 27, Ermine. 28, Gorse. 29, Dally. 31, North. 32, Decry. 34, Menu. 36, Dad. 37, Let.

PUZZLE No. 74. Across: 1, Strive. 5, Fret. 8, Value. 9, Ebb. 10, Rail. 11, Name. 12, Acted. 13, Valour. 16, Sell. 18, Alas. 20, Web. 22, Tea. 23, Lay. 24, Made. 25, Rate. 28, Expire. 30, Asset. 32, Line. 33, Vote. 34, Use. 35, Order. 36, Rank. 37, Street. **Down:** 1, Swerve. 2, Rebelled. 3, Versus. 4, Calculate. 5, Funeral. 6, Read. 7, Teem. 8, Via. 14, Retrieved. 15, Pay. 17, Lea. 19, Latitude. 20, Wan. 21, Berserk. 26, Expect. 27, Resent. 29, Blur. 30, Anon. 31, Tor.

PUZZLE No. 75. Across: 1, Trick. 5, System. 8, Remit. 10, Insane. 11, Item. 14, Remain. 15, Protest. 18, Net. 19, Urn. 21, Defy. 23, Prior. 24, Grab. 27, Eat. 29, Keg. 31, Literal. 32, Soiled. 34, Note. 35, Editor. 38, Alder. 39, Dogged. 40, Newly. **Down:** 2, Ran. 3, Crafty. 4, Ken. 5, Stir. 6, Seemed. 7, Mainly. 9, Measure. 12, Ten. 13, Mate. 16, Rear. 17, Trial. 20, Noticed. 22, Flea. 24, Gasped. 25, Akin. 26, Belong. 28, Retire. 30, Get. 33, Dead. 36, Den. 37, Oil.

PUZZLE No. 76. Across: 2, Blind. 7, Ache. 8, Unsure. 9, Tense. 11, Cad. 13, Pot. 15, Open. 16, Sob. 18, Yoke. 19, Atelier. 20, Rail. 22, Stem. 23, Vacancy. 25, Chew. 27, Yak. 28, Torn. 30, Tor. 31, Nag. 33, Beast. 36, Estate. 37, Urge. 38, Green. **Down:** 1, Scrap. 2, Bet. 3, Inn. 4, Due. 5, Asp. 6, Brook. 10, Shoe. 11, Correct. 12, Deliver. 13, Portion. 14, Teeming. 16, Stray. 17, Block. 18, Yes. 21, Law. 24, Name. 26, House. 29, Range. 32, Lay. 33, Beg. 34, Awe. 35, Tun.

PUZZLE No. 77. Across: 2, Ocean. 7, Prowl. 8, Alter. 10, Lucid. 12, Air. 13, Asset. 15, Drained. 17, Sketch. 19, Arm. 20, Hoisted. 23, Ever. 25, Dine. 26, Deficit. 30, Fad. 31, Castle. 34, Natural. 37, Layer. 38, Tot. 39, Yield. 40, Cower. 41, Elect. 42, Lorry. **Down:** 1, Brisk. 2, Owlet. 3, Clutch. 4, Avid. 5, Claimed. 6, Beret. 9, Tin. 11, Drastic. 13, Asked. 14, Sewed. 16, Art. 18, Holiday. 21, Dirty. 22, Sever. 24, Refuted. 27, Far. 28, Taller. 29, Baton. 32, Sadly. 33, Leech. 35, Tow. 36, Lido.

PUZZLE No. 78. Across: 1, Mail. 4, Cup. 6, Tack. 8, Leaner. 9, Inborn. 10, Led. 12, Banal. 14, Doubt. 15, Genre. 18, Delete. 20, Abacus. 24, Water. 26, Spare. 28, Droop. 30, Set. 32, Commit. 33, Random. 34, Test. 35, Nap. 36, Earn. **Down:** 2, Arena. 3, Lineage. 4, Curl. 5, Paid. 7, Taboo. 11, Err. 12, Bad. 13, Let. 16, New. 17, Eat. 19, Explode. 21, Bed. 22, Arrange. 23, Sip. 25, Ace. 27, Remit. 29, Odour. 30, Stun. 31, Trap.

PUZZLE No. 79. Across: 1, Sample. 5, Wished. 8, Alighted. 9, Tour. 10, Ass. 12, Label. 15, Met. 17, Tie. 18, Ode. 19, Lea. 20, Dined. 21, Ail. 22, Rug. 23, Gun. 24, Wit. 26, Ensue. 29, Toy. 33, Main. 34, Dismayed. 35, Recede. 36, Treaty. **Down:** 2, Atlas. 3, Page. 4, Extra. 5, Wedge. 6, Site. 7, Exude. 10, Allow. 11, Start. 12, Ledge. 13, Bonus. 14, Lodge. 15, Meant. 16, Tally. 25, Irate. 27, Nudge. 28, Upset. 30, Overt. 31, Once. 32, Game.

PUZZLE No. 80. Across: 1, Item. **4**, Tag. **6**, Drop. **9**, Rob. **10**, Preserve. **11**, Idea. **14**, Sat. **16**, Beset. **19**, Secluded. **21**, Money. **23**, Received. **24**, Radio. **27**, Ten. **31**, Tiff. **33**, Disperse. **34**, See. **35**, Beer. **36**, Lad. **37**, Dirt. **Down: 2**, Turn. **3**, Miss. **4**, Toreador. **5**, Grew. **6**, Drive. **7**, Rod. **8**, Obese. **12**, Astir. **13**, Acted. **14**, Sum. **15**, Tenet. **17**, Slave. **18**, Trade. **20**, Deceased. **22**, Yen. **25**, Arise. **26**, Infer. **28**, Idol. **29**, Weld. **30**, User. **32**, Fee.

PUZZLE No. 81. Across: 4, False. **7**, Esteem. **9**, Sad. **10**, Men. **12**, Doubt. **13**, Evil. **15**, Never. **17**, Deluge. **19**, Eden. **20**, Scene. **22**, Let. **24**, Desired. **27**, Sag. **28**, Named. **31**, Tall. **33**, Needle **35**, Amend. **37**, Edam. **38**, Paste. **39**, Tip. **41**, Eat. **42**, Tablet. **43**, Stern. **Down: 1**, Recess. **2**, Stride. **3**, Hem. **4**, Fade. **5**, Adore. **6**, Submerge. **8**, Menu. **11**, Negligent. **14**, Lend. **16**, Veer. **18**, Lees. **21**, Cataract. **23**, Tend. **25**, Sane. **26**, Dale. **29**, Meddle. **30**, Demote. **32**, Later. **34**, Edit. **36**, Mean. **40**, Pay.

PUZZLE No. 82. Across: 1, Raffle. **5**, Cosmic. **9**, Oaten. **10**, Caress. **11**, Actual. **12**, Terse. **14**, Reed. **17**, Doe. **18**, Lean. **20**, Dated. **22**, Sadly. **23**, Modesty. **24**, Depot. **26**, Yearn. **29**, Iron. **30**, Ate. **33**, Fiend. **35**, Stream. **36**, Rammed. **37**, Tenor. **38**, Lodged. **39**, Leaned. **Down: 1**, Record. **2**, Forget. **3**, Lost. **4**, Eased. **5**, Cease. **6**, Once. **7**, Mauled. **8**, Colony. **13**, Rosette. **15**, Eager. **16**, Demon. **18**, Layer. **19**, Alert. **21**, Dot. **22**, Sty. **24**, Diesel. **25**, Poured. **27**, Airmen. **28**, Needed. **30**, Aimed. **31**, Enrol. **33**, Fate. **34**, Dare.

PUZZLE No. 83. Across: 3, Satan. **9**, Clever. **10**, Leader. **11**, Acute. **12**, Used. **15**, Wise. **17**, Retired. **20**, Tin. **21**, Robot. **23**, Even. **25**, Disc. **26**, Dirge. **28**, Sew. **30**, Explore. **33**, Idol. **35**, Ever. **36**, Tibia. **38**, Colour. **39**, Scarce. **40**, Beset. **Down: 1**, Scour. **2**, Beret. **3**, Sea. **4**, Archer. **5**, Alto. **6**, Nee. **7**, Admit. **8**, Green. **13**, Severed. **14**, Dined. **16**, Sincere. **18**, Dodge. **19**, Hod. **22**, Title. **24**, Nil. **27**, Excise. **28**, Since. **29**, World. **31**, Overt. **32**, Erred. **34**, Tire. **36**, Tub. **37**, Act.

PUZZLE No. 84. Across: 1, Modern. **5**, Yelp. **8**, Cowed. **9**, Lot. **10**, Soon. **11**, Ague. **12**, Scare. **13**, Driver. **16**, Dear. **18**, Ewer. **20**, Wed. **22**, Gin. **23**, Dam. **24**, Made. **25**, Amen. **28**, Dented. **30**, Faint. **32**, Pray. **33**, Iota. **34**, Foe. **35**, Meant. **36**, Died. **37**, Pellet. **Down: 1**, Malady. **2**, Detailed. **3**, Risked. **4**, Concerned. **5**, Yearned. **6**, Edge. **7**, Pier. **8**, Cos. **14**, Regaining. **15**, Gem. **17**, Aim. **19**, Wasteful. **20**, Wad. **21**, Decayed. **26**, Negate. **27**, Advent. **29**, Sped. **30**, Fame. **31**, Tot.

PUZZLE No. 85. Across: 1, Slept. **5**, Resume. **8**, Ledge. **10**, Serene. **11**, Aver. **14**, Damage. **15**, Control. **18**, Net. **19**, Tap. **21**, Deft. **23**, Legal. **24**, Sect. **27**, Den. **29**, Era. **31**, Rampage. **32**, Eldest. **34**, Easy. **35**, Harass. **38**, Press. **39**, Groyne. **40**, Petty. **Down: 2**, Lee. **3**, Plenty. **4**, Ten. **5**, Read. **6**, Seemed. **7**, Expect. **9**, Demoted. **12**, Van. **13**, Rate. **16**, Ooze. **17**, Lager. **20**, Panache. **22**, Flag. **24**, Seeing. **25**, Cede. **26**, Treaty. **28**, Sparse. **30**, Ass. **33**, Type. **36**, Asp. **37**, Set.

PUZZLE No. 86. Across: 2, Hotel. **7**, Solo. **8**, Insect. **9**, Dance. **11**, Cos. **13**, Sum. **15**, Hate. **16**, Fad. **18**, Dire. **19**, Natural. **20**, Mire. **22**, Beer. **23**, Trusted. **25**, Seer. **27**, Eat. **28**, Ache. **30**, End. **31**, Ear. **33**, Skill. **36**, Recede. **37**, Open. **38**, Treat. **Down: 1**, Cocoa. **2**, Hod. **3**, Tin. **4**, Lie. **5**, Ass. **6**, Scour. **10**, Chat. **11**, Chemise. **12**, Started. **13**, Silence. **14**, Merrier. **16**, False. **17**, Duvet. **18**, Dab. **21**, Err. **24**, Tank. **26**, Enter. **29**, Hades. **32**, Wet. **33**, Set. **34**, Ire. **35**, Lot.

PUZZLE No. 87. Across: 2, Legal. **7**, Relax. **8**, Mooed. **10**, Steer. **12**, Urn. **13**, Raise. **15**, Robbery. **17**, Almond. **19**, Tit. **20**, Dreaded. **23**, Eyed. **25**, Dead. **26**, Limited. **30**, Van. **31**, Deride. **34**, Resided. **37**, Named. **38**, Bad. **39**, Depot. **40**, Jewel. **41**, Tense. **42**, Steed. **Down: 1**, Petal. **2**, Lasso. **3**, Extend. **4**, Aver. **5**, Doubted. **6**, Genre. **9**, Ore. **11**, Rotated. **13**, Raced. **14**, Impel. **16**, Bid. **18**, Drained. **21**, Denim. **22**, Edged. **24**, Divided. **27**, Mad. **28**, Denote. **29**, Rebel. **32**, Rated. **33**, Dense. **35**, Saw. **36**, Deft.

PUZZLE No. 88. Across: 1, Here. 4, Sip. 6, Teem. 8, Bungle. 9, Angler. 10, Pry. 12, Speak. 14, Stray. 15, Vista. 18, Accent. 20, Wailed. 24, Yield. 26, Press. 28, Learn. 30, Elk. 32, Marina. 33, Eulogy. 34, Glue. 35, Nip. 36, Yell. **Down:** 2 Equip. 3, Engrave. 4, Seep. 5, Pray. 6, Tight. 7, Elevate. 11, Rot. 12, Spa. 13, Kin. 16, Sty. 17, Awe. 19, Curtail. 21, All. 22, Ideally. 23, Don. 25, Ill. 27, Shine. 29, Regal. 30, Earn. 31, Keep.

PUZZLE No. 89. Across: 1, Seemed. 5, Allege. 8, Contract. 9, Meal. 10, Lea. 12, Perch. 15, Use. 17, Sea. 18, Inn. 19, Yes. 20, Given. 21, Imp. 22, Era. 23, Get. 24, Lit. 26, Nudge. 29, Eel. 33, Isle. 34, Universe. 35, Petrol. 36, Easier. **Down:** 2, Evoke. 3, Mute. 4, Drape. 5, Attic. 6, Limp. 7, Glass. 10, Loyal. 11, Asset. 12, Pagan. 13, Roved. 14, Hinge. 15, Unite. 16, Expel. 25,Issue. 27, Usual. 28, Grime. 30, Ensue. 31, Fear. 32, Mess.

PUZZLE No. 90. Across: 1, Rift. 4, Dog. 6, Pail. 9, Rim. 10, Collapse. 11, Oral. 14, Act. 16, Sewer. 19, Invented. 21, Tenor. 23, Demanded. 24, Erect. 27, Tip. 31, Rude. 33, Inactive. 34, See. 35, Mend. 36, Kit. 37, More. **Down:** 2, Iron. 3, Tall. 4, Depicted. 5, Grew. 6, Prone. 7, Air. 8, Image. 12, Title. 13, Evade. 14, Ant. 15, Tenet. 17, Windy. 18, Ready. 20, Dominant. 22, Rap. 25, Rouse. 26, Creed. 28, Sink. 29, Stem. 30, Over. 32, Den.

PUZZLE No. 91. Across: 4, Plead. 7, Custom. 9, Lie. 10, Pen. 12, Nasty. 13, Emit. 15, Never. 17, Refuge. 19, Note. 20, Scene. 22, Led. 24, Desired. 27, Lag. 28, Fated. 31, Iris. 33, Gentle. 35, Crane. 37, Earn. 38, Canoe. 39, Tap. 41, Ray. 42, Relent. 43, Level. **Down:** 1, Access. 2, Aspire. 3, Top. 4, Pine. 5, Learn. 6, Altitude. 8, Menu. 11, Negligent. 14, Tend. 16, Veer. 18, Feel. 21, Carriage. 23, Deft. 25, Saga. 26, Dale. 29, Teased. 30, Denote. 32, Score. 34, Near. 36, Real. 40, Pet.

PUZZLE No. 92. Across: 1, Rigour. 5, Bought. 9, Saver. 10, Carpet. 11, Salmon. 12, Revel. 14, Reed. 17, Dot. 18, Cove. 20, Dated. 22, Piled. 23, Notched. 24, Lease. 26, Repel. 29, Edge. 30, Met. 32, Rude. 33, Fared. 35, Seemed. 36, Nation. 37, Alter. 38, Nudity. 39, Tether. **Down:** 1, Record. 2, Garnet. 3, User. 4, Rated. 5, Beset. 6, Oral. 7, Gambol. 8, Tinted. 13, Voucher. 15, Eased. 16, Dense. 18, Cider. 19, Vexed. 21, Doe. 22, Per. 24, Lessen. 25, Agreed. 27, Punish. 28, Leaner. 30, Madly. 31, Tenet. 33, Feat. 34, Dare.

PUZZLE No. 93. Across: 3, Catch. 9, Turbot. 10, August. 11, Stole. 12, Mode. 15, Cost. 17, Present. 20, See. 21, Dived. 23, Flat. 25, West. 26, Yearn. 28, Ace. 30, Aerosol. 33, Next. 35, Tone. 36, Medal. 38, Rector. 39, Towing. 40, Beret. **Down:** 1, Stump. 2, Grade. 3, Cos. 4, Attend. 5, Calm. 6, Hue. 7, Kudos. 8, State. 13, Orifice. 14, Essay. 16, Section. 18, Tiara. 19, Sew. 22, Depot. 24, Tea. 27, Negate. 28, Angry. 29, Exact. 31, Solid. 32, Ledge. 34, Mere. 36, Mob. 37, Lot.

PUZZLE No. 94. Across: 1, Spread. 5, Dart. 8, Later. 9, Rum. 10, Omen. 11, Limp. 12, Acted. 13, Banter. 16, Deal. 18, Edit. 20, Hid. 22, Ill. 23, Don. 24, Nice. 25, Need. 28, Debate. 30, Minor. 32, Akin. 33, Rose. 34, Imp. 35, React. 36, Rued. 37, Stance. **Down:** 1, Scribe. 2, Romantic. 3, Adored. 4, Cancelled. 5, Deleted. 6, Arid. 7, Type. 8, Lea. 14, Reinforce. 15, Tin. 17, Ale. 19, Donation. 20, Hit. 21, Defined. 26, Defeat. 27, People. 29, Pair. 30, Mire. 31, Rot.

PUZZLE No. 95. Across: 1, Slept. 5, Copied. 8, Lodge. 10, Revere. 11, Dead. 14, Encode. 15, Picture. 18, Den. 19, Ear. 21, Deed. 23, Aster. 24, Weld. 27, Set. 29, Oar. 31, Niggled. 32, Chorus. 34, Knee. 35, Eroded. 38, Elder. 39, Dodder. 40, Deter. **Down:** 2, Lee. 3, Plenty. 4, Tor. 5, Cede. 6, Placed. 7, Depend. 9, Depress. 12, End. 13, Done. 16, Idle. 17, Eaten. 20, Retired. 22, Erne. 24, Wicked. 25, Look. 26, Darned. 28, Ignore. 30, Rue. 33, Seer. 36, Red. 37, Eke.

PUZZLE No. 96. Across: 2, Nudge. 7, Isle. 8, Winner. 9, Wedge. 11, Aid. 13, Mar. 15, Drew. 16, Bat. 18, Here. 19, Delayed. 20, Emit. 22, Wise. 23, Revised. 25, Eden. 27, Nod. 28, Bare. 30, Dud. 31, Lad. 33, State. 36, Active. 37, Laid. 38, Wreck. **Down:** 1, Astir. 2, New. 3, Dad. 4, Ewe. 5, Inn. 6, Debar. 10, Goal. 11, Adhered. 12, Desired. 13, Medical. 14, Revered. 16, Begin. 17, Tamed. 18, Hew. 21, Ten. 24, Sort. 26, Dunce. 29, Rapid. 32, Wit. 33, Sew. 34, Awe. 35, Elk.

PUZZLE No. 97. Across: 2, Sloth. 7, Quote. 8, Medal. 10, Other. 12, Sin. 13, Start. 15, Decided. 17, Termed. 19, Sod. 20, Refuted. 23, Need. 25, Dish. 26, Decoded. 30, Cat. 31, Debate. 34, Gleaned. 37, Renew. 38, Try. 39, Devil. 40, Beret. 41, Donor. 42, Strew. **Down:** 1, Quite. 2, Storm. 3, Letter. 4, Tied. 5, Resided. 6, Waned. 9, Did. 11, Resumed. 13, Stink. 14, Armed. 16, Cot. 18, Denoted. 21, Divan. 22, Threw. 24, Decayed. 27, Can. 28, Deride. 29, Alter. 32, Below. 33, Tenor. 35, Err. 36, Deft.

PUZZLE No. 98. Across: 1, Hung. 4, Pip. 6, Oral. 8, Divert. 9, Addled. 10, Hen. 12, Began. 14,Trial. 15, Debut. 18, Delete. 20, Edited. 24, Drain. 26, Spare. 28, Paste. 30, Led. 32, Malice. 33, Animal. 34, Once. 35, Nip. 36, Yank. **Down:** 2, Unite. 3, Grenade. 4, Path. 5, Plan. 6, Order. 7, Average. 11, Emu. 12, Bad. 13, Net. 16, Bed. 17, Tea. 19, Explain. 21, Dip. 22, Inanity. 23, Die. 25, Roe. 27, Raise. 29, Train. 30, Lean. 31, Damp.

PUZZLE No. 99. Across: 1, Asking. 5, Treaty. 8, Definite. 9, Dour. 10, Spa. 12, Offer. 15, Sty. 17, Gnu. 18, Aft. 19, Era. 20, Trait. 21, Ape. 22, Ire. 23, Eel. 24, Men. 26, Ruled. 29, Lid. 33, Just. 34, Desolate. 35, Player. 36, Expert. **Down:** 2, Steep. 3, Iris. 4, Grief. 5, Theme. 6, Eddy. 7, Trust. 10, Steam. 11, Again. 12, Outer. 13, Frail. 14, Rated. 15, Stall. 16, Yield. 25, Equal. 27, Under. 28, Ensue. 30, Inter. 31, Stay. 32, Slap.

PUZZLE No. 100. Across: 1, Stop. 4, Dog. 6, Warn. 9, Ace. 10, Dreadful. 11, Stab. 14, Wad. 16, Petty. 19, Idolater. 21, Refer. 23, Decadent. 24, Canal. 27, Row. 31, Grab. 33, Abridged. 34, Ill. 35, Idle. 36, Tee. 37, Ease. **Down:** 2, Turn. 3, Play. 4, Defeated. 5, Gulp. 6, Waste. 7, Act. 8, React. 12, Civic. 13, Dozen. 14, War. 15, Defer. 17, Tower. 18, Youth. 20, Recourse. 22, Raw. 25, Acrid. 26, Amble. 28, Cart. 29, Edge. 30, Mess. 32, All.

PUZZLE No. 101. Across: 4, Saved. 7, Esteem. 9, Wet. 10, Pet. 12, Elect. 13, Trip. 15, Arena. 17, Rested. 19, Soon. 20, Whelp. 22, Aim. 24, Fretted. 27, Yam. 28, Night. 31, Diva. 33, Sender. 35, Scene. 37, Duke. 38, Lasso. 39, Tap. 41, Era. 42, Tumble. 43, State. **Down:** 1, Bestow. 2, Attire. 3, Pep. 4, Seen. 5, Atlas. 6, Encroach. 8, Meat. 11, Treatment. 14, Pelf. 16, Edit. 18, Spry. 21, Hesitant. 23, Mend. 25, Ease. 26, Died. 29, Grubby. 30, Teemed. 32, Asset. 34, Neat. 36, Core. 40, Put.

PUZZLE No. 102. Across: 1, Unkind. 5, Priest. 9, Eagle. 10, Judder. 11, Aspect. 12, Debit. 14, Sham. 17, Den. 18, Ogle. 20, Taper. 22, Freed. 23, Relayed. 24, Tepid. 26, Nerve. 29, Emit. 30, Asp. 32, Reed. 33, Sleep. 35, Detail. 36, Ticket. 37, Total. 38, Dulcet. 39, Leader. **Down:** 1, Unjust. 2, Kidnap. 3, Need. 4, Dared. 5, Plain. 6, Rest. 7, Emerge. 8, Totted. 13, Because. 15, Harem. 16, Merit. 18, Order. 19, Leave. 21, Red. 22, Fen. 24, Tended. 25, Pistol. 27, Reeked. 28, Editor. 30, Allot. 31, Petal. 33, Site. 34, Pile.

PUZZLE No. 103. Across: 3, Start. 9, Donkey. 10, Easier. 11, Train. 12, Epic. 15, Sect. 17, Recount. 20, Woe. 21, Tower. 23, Fair. 25, Pond. 26, Cabin. 28, Ace. 30, Ceasing. 33, Stir. 35, Tree. 36, Aorta. 38, Exempt. 39, Litter. 40, Eager. **Down:** 1, Adder. 2, Antic. 3, Set. 4, Tyrant. 5, Rein. 6, Tan. 7, Sinew. 8, Trite. 13, Perfect. 14, Comic. 16, Condone. 18, Tonic. 19, Rep. 22, Roost. 24, Ram. 27, Nestle. 28, Asked. 29, Eider. 31, Irate. 32, Genre. 34, Rota. 36, Ape. 37, Air.

PUZZLE No. 104. Across: 1, Resort. 5, Good. 8, Yearn. 9, See. 10, Glee. 11, Acne. 12, Skate. 13, Elicit. 16, Name. 18, Numb. 20, Per. 22, Nap. 23, Gnu. 24, Tune. 25, Trek. 28, Relent. 30, Dealt. 32, Mood. 33, Iron. 34, Tot. 35, Messy. 36, Tied. 37, Plunge. **Down:** 1, Risked. 2, Specimen. 3, Regain. 4, Beekeeper. 5, Grating. 6, Once. 7, Deem. 8, Yes. 14, Tantalise. 15, Emu. 17, Mar. 19, Unbeaten. 20, Pup. 21, Receded. 26, Kennel. 27, Statue. 29, Omit. 30, Dome. 31, Try.

PUZZLE No. 105. Across: 1, Steer. 5, Coward. 8, Local. 10, Potato. 11, Avid. 14, Divide. 15, Rosette. 18, Men. 19, End. 21, Deft. 23, Inter. 24, Slit. 27, Ten. 29, Tin. 31, Rotated. 32, Veered. 34, Mate. 35, Elapse. 38, Aided. 39, Extend. 40, Tenet. **Down:** 2, Too. 3, Elated. 4, Rot. 5, Clad. 6, Waived. 7, Decent. 9, Content. 12, Vim. 13, Dine. 16, Oval. 17, Enter. 20, Denoted. 22, Fame. 24, Severe. 25, Item. 26, Tirade. 28, Parade. 30, Net. 33, Dead. 36, Let. 37, Sue.

PUZZLE No. 106. Across: 2, About. 7, Clad. 8, Except. 9, Dense. 11, Wed. 13, Cod. 15, Open. 16, Tor. 18, Rake. 19, General. 20, Said. 22, Glee. 23, Radical. 25, Item. 27, Day. 28, Fume. 30, Pad. 31, Sad. 33, Claim. 36, Cinema. 37, Edit. 38, Baton. **Down:** 1, Sleep. 2, Add. 3, Own. 4, Tee. 5, Ace. 6, Spook. 10, Soon. 11, Worship. 12, Desired. 13, Callous. 14, Deleted. 16, Tepid. 17, Relay. 18, Rag. 21, Dam. 24, Call. 26, Tacit. 29, Mania. 32, New. 33, Cab. 34, Act. 35, Men.

PUZZLE No. 107. Across: 2, Essay. 7, Doubt. 8, Sharp. 10, Basic. 12, End. 13, Eider. 15, Donated. 17, Loaded. 19, Net. 20, Dessert. 23, Tied. 25, Ease. 26, Defiant. 30, Cad. 31, Talent. 34, Awaited. 37, Money. 38, Aid. 39, Dumpy. 40, Piled. 41, Eager. 42, Pearl. **Down:** 1, Folio. 2, Ebbed. 3, Stared. 4, Avid. 5, Theatre. 6, Order. 9, Ant. 11, Consent. 13, Elite. 14, Dazed. 16, Nee. 18, Derided. 21, Taken. 22, Petty. 24, Decided. 27, Fat. 28, Tamper. 29, Swain. 32, Loyal. 33, Never. 35, Ail. 36, Dupe.

PUZZLE No. 108. Across: 1, Wilt. 4, Pip. 6, Save. 8, Deface. 9, Crease. 10, Apt. 12, Close. 14, Drain. 15, Irate. 18, Guitar. 20, Adored. 24, Motor. 26, Fiery. 28, Giddy. 30, Pet. 32, Torpor. 33, Elicit. 34, Omen. 35, Dim. 36, Edge. **Down:** 2, Ideal. 3, Transit. 4, Plea. 5, Pact. 6, Sheer. 7, Vestige. 11, Pit. 12, Cog. 13, Era. 16, Arm. 17, Eat. 19, Uniform. 21, Dog. 22, Orifice. 23, Dry. 25, Ode. 27, Ripen. 29, Doing. 30, Prod. 31, Team.

PUZZLE No. 109. Across: 1, Groped. 5, Spread. 8, Advocate. 9, Stem. 10, Cos. 12, Stall. 15, Cat. 17, Lap. 18, Ill. 19, Ado. 20, Overt. 21, Orb. 22, Par. 23, Hat. 24, Tie. 26, Title. 29, Hue. 33, Keep. 34, Brandish. 35, Statue. 36, Treaty. **Down:** 2, Radio. 3, Plot. 4, Dealt. 5, Smell. 6, Risk. 7, Arena. 10, Craft. 11, Slope. 12, Sport. 13, Avert. 14, Lithe. 15, Cloth. 16, Table. 25, Inept. 27, Imbue. 28, Least. 30, Upset. 31, Spot. 32, Idle.

PUZZLE No. 110. Across: 1, Tell. 4, Row. 6, Fate. 9, Ewe. 10, Discover. 11, Tent. 14, Bar. 16, Adore. 19, Detailed. 21, Defer. 23, Delegate. 24, Range. 27, Rip. 31, More. 33, Inactive. 34, Due. 35, Seen. 36, Die. 37, Pert. **Down:** 2, Emit. 3, Lack. 4, Revealed. 5, Warp. 6, Fetid. 7, Awe. 8, Tenor. 12, Adder. 13, Stain. 14, Bid. 15, Refer. 17, Organ. 18, Excel. 20, Delicate. 22, Rep. 25, Abode. 26, Green. 28, Mind. 29, Stop. 30, Aver. 32, Rue.

PUZZLE No. 111. Across: 4, Pupil. 7, Allege. 9, Fan. 10, Ore. 12, Rifle. 13, Iris. 15, Onset. 17, Chaste. 19, Erne. 20, Creep. 22, Rap. 24, Debated. 27, Den. 28, Erase. 31, Pier. 33, Scaled. 35, After. 37, Wood. 38, State. 39, Dip. 41, Ill. 42, Demean. 43, Drool. **Down:** 1, Maniac. 2, Plaice. 3, Ego. 4, Pare. 5, Unite. 6, Idleness. 8, Eros. 11, Entranced. 14, Shed. 16, Seat. 18, Aped. 21, Register. 23, Peel. 25, Best. 26, Drew. 29, Adored. 30, Ending. 32, Ratio. 34, Arid. 36, Fell. 40, Pet.

PUZZLE No. 112. Across: 1, Rumple. **5,** Unrest. **9,** Inane. **10,** Wedged. **11,** Waiter. **12,** Fewer. **14,** Road. **17,** Did. **18,** Fire. **20,** Dined. **22,** Allot. **23,** Bondage. **24,** Remit. **26,** Eerie. **29,** Edit. **30,** Ant. **32,** Tuna. **33,** Tiger. **35,** Period. **36,** Neaten. **37,** Terse. **38,** Darted. **39,** Eluded. **Down: 1,** Reward. **2,** Madman. **3,** Lief. **4,** Ended. **5,** Unwed. **6,** Near. **7,** Entail. **8,** Target. **13,** Winding. **15,** Oiled. **16,** Debit. **18,** Fleet. **19,** Robin. **21,** Dot. **22,** Age. **24,** Reaped. **25,** Mirror. **27,** Rusted. **28,** Earned. **30,** Aided. **31,** Tense. **33,** Tote. **34,** Reel.

PUZZLE No. 113. Across: 3, Score. **9,** Roller. **10,** Effort. **11,** Tenet. **12,** Mess. **15,** Mere. **17,** Execute. **20,** Rep. **21,** Erupt. **23,** Used. **25,** Tune. **26,** Water. **28,** Fed. **30,** Devoted. **33,** Idea. **35,** Ride. **36,** Pique. **38,** Alfoat. **39,** Series. **40,** Level. **Down: 1,** Grime. **2,** Close. **3,** Set. **4,** Create. **5,** Reed. **6,** Eft. **7,** Cower. **8,** Steep. **13,** Excused. **14,** Screw. **16,** Receded. **18,** Erred. **19,** Apt. **22,** Tutor. **24,** Dam. **27,** Refuse. **28,** Final. **29,** Dealt. **31,** Timid. **32,** Dense. **34,** Site. **36,** Pal. **37,** Eel.

PUZZLE No. 114. Across: 1, Impede. **5,** Sham. **8,** Voice. **9,** Sin. **10,** Vain. **11,** Rate. **12,** Asset. **13,** Detour. **16,** Tern. **18,** Edam. **20,** End. **22,** Fit. **23,** Dog. **24,** Fate. **25,** Eden. **28,** Design. **30,** Revel. **32,** Beat. **33,** Neat. **34,** Ire. **35,** React. **36,** Eyed. **37,** Recent. **Down: 1,** Inside. **2,** Penitent. **3,** Devout. **4,** Consented. **5,** Screwed. **6,** Heat. **7,** Meet. **8,** Via. **14,** Reference. **15,** Lag. **17,** Rid. **19,** Domicile. **20,** Eat. **21,** Deleted. **26,** Nestle. **27,** Intent. **29,** Able. **30,** Rare. **31,** Let.

PUZZLE No. 115. Across: 1, Erect. **5,** Feeble. **8,** Haste. **10,** Report. **11,** Emit. **14,** Latent. **15,** Concept. **18,** Pea. **19,** Pad. **21,** Dray. **23,** Below. **24,** Slot. **27,** Don. **29,** Pig. **31,** Natural. **32,** Veered. **34,** Name. **35,** Eroded. **38,** Adder. **39,** Extend. **40,** Demur. **Down: 2,** Rue. **3,** Choice. **4,** Tar. **5,** Feel. **6,** Exited. **7,** Earthy. **9,** Stopped. **12,** Map. **13,** Tear. **16,** Oral. **17,** Talon. **20,** Donated. **22,** Area. **24,** Severe. **25,** Open. **26,** Tirade. **28,** Furore. **30,** Gem. **33,** Dead. **36,** Red. **37,** Emu.

PUZZLE No. 116. Across: 2, Amend. **7,** Eros. **8,** Unload. **9,** Shape. **11,** Sad. **13,** Rue. **15,** Eden. **16,** Pea. **18,** Deem. **19,** Drastic. **20,** Tool. **22,** Else. **23,** Severed. **25,** Edit. **27,** Din. **28,** Undo. **30,** Rut. **31,** Err. **33,** Began. **36,** Active. **37,** Unit. **38,** Depot. **Down: 1,** Broad. **2,** Ass. **3,** Era. **4,** Due. **5,** Sly. **6,** Vague. **10,** Plea. **11,** Settler. **12,** Deposit. **13,** Recline. **14,** Emperor. **16,** Pried. **17,** Ashen. **18,** Die. **21,** Let. **24,** Rise. **26,** Dunce. **29,** Drain. **32,** Nip. **33,** Bed. **34,** Gap. **35,** Nut.

PUZZLE No. 117. Across: 2, Dally. **7,** Hades. **8,** Asked. **10,** Blend. **12,** Hit. **13,** Issue. **15,** Donated. **17,** Settee. **19,** Dam. **20,** Pledged. **23,** Edam. **25,** Draw. **26,** Discord. **30,** Net. **31,** Yelled. **34,** Awaited. **37,** False. **38,** Elm. **39,** Debit. **40,** Value. **41,** Legal. **42,** Order. **Down: 1,** Raise. **2,** Debut. **3,** Asleep. **4,** Land. **5,** Ashamed. **6,** Deter. **9,** Kit. **11,** Doddery. **13,** Islet. **14,** Stead. **16,** Nag. **18,** Elected. **21,** Drill. **22,** Swede. **24,** Minimum. **27,** Set. **28,** Defile. **29,** Swear. **32,** Later. **33,** Essay. **35,** All. **36,** Dear.

PUZZLE No. 118. Across: 1, Rota. **4,** Gun. **6,** Lout. **8,** Chaste. **9,** Advice. **10,** Eat. **12,** Aroma. **14,** Grave. **15,** Evoke. **18,** Murder. **20,** Nature. **24,** Badge. **26,** Hardy. **28,** Eagle. **30,** Pet. **32,** Lawful. **33,** Adhere. **34,** Beer. **35,** Tie. **36,** Rued. **Down: 2,** Other. **3,** Assumed. **4,** Glee. **5,** Neat. **6,** Lover. **7,** Uncover. **11,** Ask. **12,** Aim. **13,** Ave. **16,** Orb. **17,** End. **19,** Unaware. **21,** Age. **22,** Teacher. **23,** Eke. **25,** Ace. **27,** Defer. **29,** Large. **30,** Plot. **31,** Tame.

PUZZLE No. 119. Across: 1, Target. **5,** Severe. **8,** Converge. **9,** Rout. **10,** Web. **12,** Cheer. **15,** Den. **17,** Oar. **18,** Air. **19,** Tea. **20,** Alien. **21,** Auk. **22,** Raw. **23,** Gem. **24,** Rid. **26,** Lithe. **29,** And. **33,** Item. **34,** Patience. **35,** Brutal. **36,** Dither. **Down: 2,** Adore. **3,** Ogle. **4,** Give. **5,** Torch. **5,** Scene. **6,** Vary. **7,** Rouse. **10,** Water. **11,** Board. **12,** Crawl. **13,** Evict. **14,** Range. **15,** Drama. **16,** Naked. **25,** Inter. **27,** Impel. **28,** Hated. **30,** Niche. **31,** Emit. **32,** Pest.

PUZZLE No. 120. Across: 1, Pant. 4, Sum. 6, Step. 9, Tor. 10, Delegate. 11, Apex. 14, Awe. 16, Unity. 19, Moorland. 21, Erred. 23, Toboggan. 24, Kitty. 27, Log. 31, Jeer. 33, Examiner. 34, Aye. 35, Fled. 36, Par. 37, Doll. **Down:** 2, Aped. 3, Teem. 4, Stalwart. 5, Meet. 6, Stain. 7, Top. 8, Erect. 12, Smack. 13, Boast. 14, Ale. 15, Enrol. 17, Image. 18, Young. 20, Debonair. 22, Dog. 25, Ideal. 26, Tired. 28, Keep. 29, Find. 30, Yell. 32, Eye.

PUZZLE No. 121. Across: 4, Grasp. 7, Gratis. 9, Woe. 10, Rod. 12, Avert. 13, Ewer. 15, Lisle. 17, Repose. 19, Lane. 20, Diner. 22, Cat. 24, Donated. 27, Per. 28, Arena. 31, Miss. 33, Adored. 35, Water. 37, Will. 38, Harem. 39, Dam. 41, Aid. 42, Lolled. 43, Heard. **Down:** 1, Agreed. 2, Cavern. 3, Fir. 4, Goal. 5, Revel. 6, Shrunken. 8, Solo. 11, Discarded. 14, Reed. 16, Seat. 18, Prop. 21, Indicate. 23, Tear. 25, Neat. 26, Drew. 29, Edible. 30, Allude. 32, Swear. 34, Oral. 36, Amid. 40, Mob.

PUZZLE No. 122. Across: 1, Recess. 5, Hamper. 9, Ocean. 10, Pillar. 11, Volume. 12, Raven. 14, Sham. 17, Pen. 18, Here. 20, Tired. 22, Faded. 23, Retired. 24, Resin. 26, Debut. 29, Edit. 30, Sop. 32, Sore. 33, Waned. 35, Detail. 36, Tinder. 37, Polar. 38, Redden. 39, Leader. **Down:** 1, Repast. 2, Cellar. 3, Soar. 4, Scrap. 5, Haven. 6, Anon. 7, Paused. 8, Reeled. 13, Venison. 15, Hired. 16, Merit. 18, Hades. 19, Recur. 21, Den. 22, Fed. 24, Render. 25, Sifted. 27, Bonded. 28, Terror. 30, Salon. 31, Petal. 33, Wipe. 34, Dire.

PUZZLE No. 123. Across: 3, About. 9, Parade. 10, Sordid. 11, Other. 12, Also. 15, Dial. 17, Resided. 20, Try. 21, Regal. 23, Seen. 25, Rota. 26, Divan. 28, Arc. 30, Revenge. 33, Beat. 35, Rued. 36, Molar. 38, Scarab. 39, Tissue. 40, Toyed. **Down:** 1, Spear. 2, Gross. 3, Ado. 4, Better. 5, Used. 6, Tor. 7, Admit. 8, Oddly. 13, Leisure. 14, Oiled. 16, Arrange. 18, Debar. 19, Par. 22, Lover. 24, Nil. 27, Negate. 28, Abase. 29, Canal. 31, Nurse. 32, Edged. 34, Hobo. 36, Mat. 37, Rid.

PUZZLE No. 124. Across: 1, Except. 5, Aped. 8, Sense. 9, Can. 10, Lees. 11, Prow. 12, Asset. 13, Toiled. 16, Tern. 18, Stem. 20, Due. 22, Log. 23, Era. 24, Mien. 25, Item. 28, Ravage. 30, Tight. 32, Meet. 33, Torn. 34, Urn. 35, Sleep. 36, Gate. 37, Greedy. **Down:** 1, Excite. 2, Continue. 3, Pullet. 4, Messenger. 5, Asperse. 6, Pert. 7, Dawn. 8, Sea. 14, Delighted. 15, Tea. 17, Rot. 19, Treasure. 20, Dim. 21, Entitle. 26, Manner. 27, Keenly. 29, Smug. 30, Test. 31, Top.

PUZZLE No. 125. Across: 1, Slept. 5, Taught. 8, Risky. 10, Street. 11, Pole. 14, Eroded. 15, Attempt. 18, Bag. 19, Pad. 21, Dear. 23, Depot. 24, Mess. 27, Din. 29, Lap. 31, Radical. 32, Shiver. 34, Date. 35, Easily. 38, Nudge. 39, Relent. 40, Edict. **Down:** 2, Lot. 3, Prefer. 4, Tie. 5, Type. 6, Unload. 7, Tender. 9, Stopped. 12, Orb. 13, Edge. 16, Tale. 17, Tapir. 20, Donated. 22, Area. 24, Master. 25, Slid. 26, Savage. 28, Missed. 30, Pet. 33, Rent. 36, Age. 37, Lac.

PUZZLE No. 126. Across: 2, Creek. 7, Gala. 8, Estate. 9, Ready. 11, Ill. 13, Did. 15, Mood. 16, Bow. 18, Sere. 19, Perhaps. 20, Tear. 22, Yell. 23, Timidly. 25, Tied. 27, Nip. 28, Over. 30, End. 31, Eye. 33, Heave. 36, Remove. 37, Raid. 38, Water. **Down:** 1, Hallo. 2, Car. 3, Era. 4, Key. 5, Ate. 6, Stair. 10, Door. 11, Imitate. 12, Located. 13, Deserve. 14, Declare. 16, Begin. 17, Whelp. 18, Spy. 21, Rid. 24, Dive. 26, Inter. 29, Eyrie. 32, Cow. 33, Hew. 34, Aft. 35, Err

PUZZLE No. 127. Across: 2, Phial. 7, Villa. 8, Adore. 10, Angel. 12, Aid. 13, Staid. 15, Rumpled. 17, Larder. 19, Cat. 20, Defined. 23, Eyed. 25, Deft. 26, Derived. 30, Sad. 31, Recite. 34, Awaited. 37, Dated. 38, Fir. 39, Demur. 40, Lured. 41, Cease. 42, Greed. **Down:** 1, Vista. 2, Plaid. 3, Handed. 4, Aver. 5, Adapted. 6, Order. 9, Oil. 11, Lucifer. 13, Sleep. 14, Armed. 16, Man. 18, Resided. 21, Debit. 22, Steed. 24, Desired. 27, Rat. 28, Deduce. 29, Awful. 32, Cared. 33, Tense. 35, Air. 36, Dear.

PUZZLE No. 128. Across: 1. Aged. 4. Pad. 6. Huge. 8. Dapper. 9. Mature. 10. Tap. 12, Below. 14. Cheap. 15, Rebel. 18. Delete. 20, Elated. 24, Dream. 26, Spare. 28, Paste. 30, Apt. 32, Colour. 33, Elicit. 34, Deft. 35, Dud. 36, Grew. **Down:** 2, Grade. 3, Deplore. 4, Pert. 5, Dump. 6, Hitch. 7, Garbage. 11, Ale. 12, Bad. 13, Wet. 16, Bed. 17, Lee. 19, Explode. 21, Lap. 22, Amazing. 23, Due. 25, Rip. 27, Roost. 29, Trite. 30, Arid. 31, Tend.

PUZZLE No. 129. Across: 1, Battle. 5, Astute. 8, Dominate. 9, Apex. 10, Web. 12, Regal. 15, Peg. 17, Lea. 18, Use. 19, Axe. 20, Train. 21, Tie. 22, Sue. 23, Get. 24, Yes. 26, Dodge. 29, Yen. 33, Vent. 34, Nauseous. 35, Stupor. 36, Easily. **Down:** 2, Arose. 3, Trip. 4, Erase. 5, Arena. 6, Trap. 7, Theme. 10, Weary. 11, Bless. 12, Rated. 13, Grand. 14, Lunge. 15, Petty. 16, Green. 25, Event. 27, Owner. 28, Gauge. 30, Equal. 31, Stop. 32, Less.

PUZZLE No. 130. Across: 1, Span. 4, Dam. 6, Hack. 9, Ail. 10, Deceased. 11, Smug. 14, Cur. 16, Verge. 19, Promoted. 21, Defer. 23, Deformed. 24, Terse. 27, Red. 31, Ruse. 33, Outdated. 34, Den. 35, Seed. 36, Mad. 37, Ease. **Down:** 2, Peer. 3, Need. 4, Disputed. 5, Made. 6, Haste. 7, Aim. 8, Clung. 12, Sport. 13, Motor. 14, Cod. 15, Refer. 17, Roomy. 18, Evade. 20, Defeated. 22, Rod. 25, Exude. 26, Spend. 28, Doom. 29, Bare. 30, Mess. 32, See.

PUZZLE No. 131. Across: 4, Twist. 7, Asleep. 9, Vic. 10, Bed. 12, Minor. 13, Eros. 15, Rider. 17, Strife. 19, Dear. 20, Untie. 22, Fen. 24, Receded. 27, For. 28, Erect. 31, Data. 33, Mended. 35, Scene. 37, Wise. 38, Ditto. 39, Tap. 41, Era. 42, Recent. 43, Heard. **Down:** 1, Gateau. 2, Almost. 3, Web. 4, Time. 5, Weird. 6, Sporadic. 8, Peri. 11, Different. 14, Stir. 16, Deed. 18, Reef. 21, Negative. 23, Need. 25, Come. 26, Drew. 29, Edited. 30, Treaty. 32, Aster. 34, Near. 36, Cord. 40, Pet.

PUZZLE No. 132. Across: 1, Dodged. 5, Tended. 9, Valid. 10, Tamper. 11, Misuse. 12, Remit. 14, Char. 17, Dad. 18, Mere. 20, Honed. 22, Pedal. 23, Boasted. 24, Seven. 26, Waded. 29, Idol. 30, Lad. 32, Lane. 33, Talon. 35, Picked. 36, Noised. 37, Allot. 38, Endure. 39, Really. **Down:** 1, Detach. 2, Demean. 3, Ever. 4, Dared. 5, Timid. 6, Edit. 7, Daubed. 8, Diesel. 13, Marshal. 15, Hoped. 16, Rebel. 18, Medal. 19, Raven. 21, Don. 22, Pew. 24, Simple. 25, Voiced. 27, Damsel. 28, Deadly. 30, Ladle. 31, Donor. 33, Tear. 34, Note.

PUZZLE No. 133. Across: 3, Yacht. 9, Litter. 10, Ailing. 11, Stain. 12, Prod. 15, Role. 17, Tedious. 20, Tie. 21, Later. 23, Play. 25, Tore. 26, Never. 28, Sty. 30, Diagram. 33, Peel. 35, Hole. 36, Ready. 38, Terror. 39, Lesson. 40, Tenet. **Down:** 1, Slept. 2, Stood. 3, Yes. 4, Artful. 5, Hail. 6, Tin. 7, Pilot. 8, Agree. 13, Respite. 14, Divan. 16, Literal. 18, Saved. 19, Met. 22, Rough. 24, Yew. 27, Riddle. 28, Spate. 29, Yearn. 31, Rouse. 32, Meant. 34, Here. 36, Rot. 37, Yet.

PUZZLE No. 134. Across: 1, Depict. 5, Scan. 8, Touch. 9, Too. 10, Even. 11, Halt. 12, Asset. 13, Impair. 16, Tern. 18, Evil. 20, Act. 22, Mat. 23, Dam. 24, Alto. 25, Item. 28, Damage. 30, First. 32, Chic. 33, Iota. 34, Ire. 35, Rayon. 36, Reel. 37, Seance. **Down:** 1, Detain. 2, Prospect. 3, Credit. 4, Consented. 5, Schemed. 6, Chat. 7, Note. 8, Tea. 14, Remission. 15, Vim. 17, Rat. 19, Vacation. 20, All. 21, Topical. 26, Manage. 27, Recede. 29, Scar. 30, Fire. 31, Ton.

PUZZLE No. 135. Across: 1, Crush. 5, Easier. 8, Tired. 10, Berate. 11, Arid. 14, Malice. 15, Deleted. 18, Per. 19, Wed. 21, Dell. 23, Gaped. 24, Held. 27, Lot. 29, Ail. 31, Trample. 32, Target. 34, Deer. 35, Crease. 38, Acted. 39, Deftly. 40, Petty. **Down:** 2, Rue. 3, Stated. 4, Hit. 5, Edam. 6, Soiled. 7, Reveal. 9, Renewal. 12, Rap. 13, Dire. 16, Erne. 17, Depot. 20, Detract. 22, Loll. 24, Hatred. 25, Lard. 26, Digest. 28, Impede. 30, Lee. 33, Tray. 36, Rep. 37, Set.

PUZZLE No. 136. Across: 2, Acted. **7**, Well. **8**, Obtain. **9**, Loose. **11**, Pet. **13**, Cap. **15**, Leak. **16**, Dad. **18**, Solo. **19**, General. **20**, Nigh. **22**, Glut. **23**, Liberal. **25**, Eked. **27**, Ray. **28**, Ache. **30**, Did. **31**, Tun. **33**, Climb. **36**, Ostler. **37**, Away. **38**, Yield. **Down: 1**, Melee. **2**, All. **3**, Too. **4**, Doe. **5**, Ate. **6**, Final. **10**, Scan. **11**, Planned. **12**, Tangled. **13**, Collect. **14**, Postmen. **16**, Deter. **17**, Delay. **18**, Sag. **21**, Hid. **24**, Rail. **26**, Kiosk. **29**, Human. **32**, Ale. **33**, Cry. **34**, Ire. **35**, Bad.

PUZZLE No. 137. Across: 2, Width. **7**, Steam. **8**, Refer. **10**, Spied. **12**, Lid. **13**, Grate. **15**, Reputed. **17**, Recede. **19**, Sad. **20**, Expired. **23**, Eros. **25**, Dire. **26**, Refined. **30**, Mat. **31**, Deride. **34**, Resided. **37**, Petal. **38**, Ran. **39**, Droop. **40**, Repay. **41**, Sewer. **42**, Impel. **Down: 1**, Store. **2**, Waste. **3**, Impede. **4**, Tier. **5**, Deluded. **6**, Ceded. **9**, Fit. **11**, Desired. **13**, Greed. **14**, Actor. **16**, Par. **18**, Excited. **21**, Digit. **22**, Level. **24**, Seminar. **27**, Fad. **28**, Depose. **29**, Beret. **32**, Repel. **33**, Dated. **35**, Sap. **36**, Drum

PUZZLE No. 138. Across: 1, Calm. **4**, Jog. **6**, Step. **8**, Assume. **9**, Parade. **10**, Roe. **12**, Meant. **14**, Merry. **15**, Eager. **18**, Bridge. **20**, United. **24**, Mined. **26**, Anger. **28**, Tired. **30**, End. **32**, Florid. **33**, Rather. **34**, Stir. **35**, Yap. **36**, Cute. **Down: 2**, Aisle. **3**, Mourned. **4**, Jeer. **5**, Gape. **6**, Surge. **7**, Endorse. **11**, Ore. **12**, Mob. **13**, Tag. **16**, Gem. **17**, Run. **19**, Ringlet. **21**, Net. **22**, Idiotic. **23**, Dud. **25**, Inn. **27**, Error. **29**, Eject. **30**, Eddy. **31**, Drip

PUZZLE No. 139. Across: 1, Hectic. **5**, Talked. **8**, Desolate. **9**, Ring. **10**, Sty. **12**, State. **15**, Bid. **17**, Out. **18**, Ace. **19**, Emu. **20**, Utter. **21**, Sea. **22**, Nun. **23**, Tie. **24**, Rug. **26**, Torch. **29**, Tot. **33**, Edge. **34**, Deplored. **35**, Crater. **36**, Estate. **Down: 2**, Erect. **3**, Tool. **4**, Chart. **5**, Treat. **6**, Lard. **7**, Ennui. **10**, Steer. **11**, Young. **12**, Stunt. **13**, Alter. **14**, Earth. **15**, Beset. **16**, Draft. **25**, Under. **27**, Order. **28**, Copse. **30**, Overt. **31**, Bent. **32**, Rout.

PUZZLE No. 140. Across: 1, Oral. **4**, Sew. **6**, Open. **9**, Fen. **10**, Converse. **11**, Tart. **14**, Pad. **16**, Angle. **19**, Redeemer. **21**, Rebel. **23**, Ratified. **24**, Merge. **27**, Rip. **31**, Cure. **33**, Oriental. **34**, Due. **35**, Seen. **36**, Gag. **37**, Part. **Down: 2**, Rook. **3**, Love. **4**, Streamer. **5**, Weep. **6**, Often. **7**, Pea. **8**, Enrol. **12**, Dream. **13**, Adder. **14**, Per. **15**, Debar. **17**, Grain. **18**, Evade. **20**, Retiring. **22**, Lip. **25**, Exude. **26**, Green. **28**, Long. **29**, Snap. **30**, Fair. **32**, Rue.

PUZZLE No. 141. Across: 4, Marry. **7**, Taxing. **9**, Bed. **10**, Dad. **12**, Noble. **13**, Eden. **15**, Lemur. **17**, Rebate. **19**, Note. **20**, Motto. **22**, Era. **24**, Torrent. **27**, Rim. **28**, Order. **31**, Area. **33**, Dinner. **35**, Scene. **37**, Kill. **38**, Quota. **39**, Eel. **41**, Irk. **42**, Delete. **43**, Genre. **Down: 1**, Stream. **2**, Expert. **3**, End. **4**, Menu. **5**, Adorn. **6**, Relative. **8**, Gala. **11**, Determine. **14**, Nett. **16**, Mere. **18**, Boor. **21**, Overture. **23**, Anon. **25**, Ride. **26**, Trek. **29**, Driver. **30**, Roller. **32**, Astir. **34**, Need. **36**, Care. **40**, Led.

PUZZLE No. 142. Across: 1, Growth. **5**, Beaten. **9**, Roved. **10**, Retain. **11**, Gifted. **12**, Merit. **14**, Seem. **17**, Den. **18**, Here. **20**, Hated **22**, Bared. **23**, Dilated. **24**, Clean. **26**, Tenet. **29**, Real. **30**, Wed **32**, Sore. **33**, Rider. **35**, Vendor. **36**, Target. **37**, Lever. **38**, Dodged. **39**, Rented. **Down: 1**, Garish. **2**, Outlet. **3**, Trim. **4**, Honed. **5**, Begin. **6**, Edit. **7**, Totter. **8**, Nudged. **13**, Relaxed. **15**, Eagle. **16**, Medal. **18**, Hades. **19**, Refer. **21**, Din. **22**, Bet. **24**, Craved. **25**, Earned. **27**, Nought. **28**, Tested. **30**, Wired. **31**, Deter. **33**, Role. **34**, Rare.

PUZZLE No. 143. Across: 3, Legal. **9**, Hatred. **10**, Vanish. **11**, Tired. **12**, Data. **15**, Rota. **17**, Erected. **20**, Rap. **21**, Dress. **23**, Iron. **25**, Pair. **26**, Rigid. **28**, Sly. **30**, Negated. **33**, Peer. **35**, Nude. **36**, Debut. **38**, Turgid. **39**, Ragout. **40**, Defer. **Down: 1**, Chide. **2**, State. **3**, Let. **4**, Edited. **5**, Aver. **6**, Lad. **7**, Minor. **8**, Cheap. **13**, Article. **14**, Actor. **16**, Tarried. **18**, Drain. **19**, Asp. **22**, Satan. **24**, Nip. **27**, Demure. **28**, Spate. **29**, Yearn. **31**, Tutor. **32**, Death. **34**, Cede. **36**, Did. **37**, Tar.

PUZZLE No. 144. Across: 1, Snatch. **5**, Scum. **8**, Touch. **9**, Rut. **10**, Moon. **11**, Hall. **12**, Offer. **13**, Second. **16**, Grid. **18**, Edam. **20**, Per. **22**, Ore. **23**, Dim. **24**, Fire. **25**, Mend. **28**, Temper. **30**, Elude. **32**, Rule. **33**, Alto. **34**, Tot. **35**, Stark. **36**, Glee. **37**, Leader. **Down: 1**, Stress. **2**, Attacker. **3**, Coming. **4**, Confident. **5**, Schemed. **6**, Char. **7**, Melt. **8**, Too. **14**, Dromedary. **15**, Ram. **17**, Ire. **19**, Disputed. **20**, Pit. **21**, Replete. **26**, Demote. **27**, Crater. **29**, Brag. **30**, Else. **31**, Elk.

PUZZLE No. 145. Across: 1, Lasso. **5**, Sordid. **8**, Ideal. **10**, Seamen. **11**, Omen. **14**, Talent. **15**, Scolded. **18**, Tea. **19**, Red. **21**, Drum. **23**, Rebel. **24**, Bear. **27**, Dip. **29**, Gem. **31**, Tousled. **32**, Gauged. **34**, Erne. **35**, Eluded. **38**, Eider. **39**, Roster. **40**, Genus. **Down: 2**, Ape. **3**, Simple. **4**, Ode. **5**, Slot. **6**, Reeled. **7**, Dictum. **9**, Entered. **12**, Mat. **13**, Near. **16**, Core. **17**, Debit. **20**, Deposed. **22**, Urge. **24**, Beggar. **25**, Ague. **26**, Regret. **28**, Assure. **30**, Men. **33**, Deer. **36**, Leg. **37**, Emu.

PUZZLE No. 146. Across: 2, Light. **7**, Zero. **8**, Indeed. **9**, Genre. **11**, Set. **13**, Cog. **15**, Crib. **16**, Par. **18**, Sore. **19**, Ordinal. **20**, Edge. **22**, Glut. **23**, Laconic. **25**, Ewer. **27**, Fed. **28**, Ogle. **30**, Did. **31**, Eel. **33**, Stall. **36**, Scribe. **37**, Ergo. **38**, Wedge. **Down: 1**, Sever. **2**, Log. **3**, Gun. **4**, Tie. **5**, Odd. **6**, Tenor. **10**, Road. **11**, Screwed. **12**, Tingled. **13**, College. **14**, Genteel. **16**, Proof. **17**, Rigid. **18**, Sag. **21**, Ear. **24**, Neat. **26**, Wince. **29**, Ledge. **32**, Wit. **33**, Sew. **34**, Add. **35**, Lee.

PUZZLE No. 147. Across: 2, Edict. **7**, Spare. **8**, Renew. **10**, Razor. **12**, Lip. **13**, Actor. **15**, Defiled. **17**, Hearty. **19**, Pig. **20**, Healthy. **23**, Amid. **25**, Torn. **26**, Tarried. **30**, Man. **31**, Detest. **34**, Dreamer. **37**, Value. **38**, Bag. **39**, Devil. **40**, Later. **41**, Solve. **42**, Green. **Down: 1**, Space. **2**, Error. **3**, Dearth. **4**, Clod. **5**, Delight. **6**, Repel. **9**, Nil. **11**, Replied. **13**, Ahead. **14**, Tacit. **16**, Fit. **18**, Yearned. **21**, Yokel. **22**, Unite. **24**, Damaged. **27**, Ram. **28**, Devise. **29**, Urban. **32**, Talon. **33**, Suave. **35**, Eat. **36**, Rear.

PUZZLE No. 148. Across: 1, Slap. **4**, Bad. **6**, Sect. **8**, Morose. **9**, Ailing. **10**, Rag. **12**, Below. **14**, Defer. **15**, Tamed. **18**, Revere. **20**, Easily. **24**, Tense. **26**, Sport. **28**, Heart. **30**, Ode. **32**, Larger. **33**, Scheme. **34**, Once. **35**, Lay. **36**, Dear. **Down: 2**, Loose. **3**, Promote. **4**, Beer. **5**, Drag. **6**, Salve. **7**, Conceal. **11**, Awe. **12**, Bar. **13**, War. **16**, Met. **17**, Den. **19**, Explain. **21**, Ash. **22**, Seethed. **23**, Yet. **25**, End. **27**, Rogue. **29**, Rumba. **30**, Oral. **31**, Espy.

PUZZLE No. 149. Across: 1, Barter. **5**, Wrench. **8**, Dominant. **9**, Ripe. **10**, Raw. **12**, Chart. **15**, Dry. **17**, Oil. **18**, Ace. **19**, Dim. **20**, Ideal. **21**, Ape. **22**, Elm. **23**, Lot. **24**, Own. **26**, Badly. **29**, Hod. **33**, Sort. **34**, Tortured. **35**, Keeper. **36**, Estate. **Down: 2**, Aroma. **3**, Tail. **4**, Reach. **5**, Water. **6**, Earl. **7**, Caper. **10**, Radio. **11**, Women. **12**, Climb. **13**, Amend. **14**, Tally. **15**, Death. **16**, Yield. **25**, Whole. **27**, Alter. **28**, Large. **30**, Overt. **31**, Stop. **32**, Just

PUZZLE No. 150. Across: 1, Pass. **4**, Cow. **6**, Sash. **9**, Pit. **10**, Convince. **11**, Idol. **14**, Fur. **16**, Revel. **19**, Streamer. **21**, Demon. **23**, Diminish. **24**, Dream. **27**, Tap. **31**, Film. **33**, Interior. **34**, See. **35**, Read. **36**, Arc. **37**, Poor. **Down: 2**, Anon. **3**, Save. **4**, Consumed. **5**, Weep. **6**, Spine. **7**, Aid. **8**, Stole. **12**, Asked. **13**, Trade. **14**, Fad. **15**, Remit.. **17**, Valid. **18**, Lithe. **20**, Romantic. **22**, Nip. **25**, Raise. **26**, Aimed **28**, Diva. **29**, Drop. **30**, Solo. **32**, Lea.

PUZZLE No. 151. Across: 4, Start. **7**, Teeter. **9**, Woe. **10**, God. **12**, Leave. **13**, Plea. **15**, Beset. **17**, Arrest. **19**, Hell. **20**, Rodeo. **22**, Paw. **24**, Alleged. **27**, Ear. **28**, Learn. **31**, Kris. **33**, Tablet. **35**, Piety. **37**, Post. **38**, Debar. **39**, Err. **41**, Row. **42**, Easier. **43**, Ashen. **Down: 1**, Stupor. **2**, Behead. **3**, Peg. **4**, Sole. **5**, Teeth. **6**, Revolver. **8**, Robe. **11**, Desperate. **14**, Area. **16**, Stag. **18**, Role. **21**, Overseas. **23**, Well. **25**, Late. **26**, Deep. **29**, Atomic. **30**, Nature. **32**, Spare. **34**, Byre. **36**, Iron. **40**, Ram.

PUZZLE No. 152. Across: 1, Finest. **5,** Hector. **9,** Piled. **10,** Neater. **11,** Advent. **12,** Decry. **14,** Seer. **17,** Dad. **18,** Beer. **20,** Hades. **22,** Laden. **23,** Mariner. **24,** Attic. **26,** Tepid. **29,** Shut. **30,** Wed. **32,** Deer. **33,** Fetid. **35,** Ignore. **36,** Numbed. **37,** Edged. **38,** Nudity. **39,** Delete. **Down: 1,** Finish. **2,** Neared. **3,** Sped. **4,** Tired. **5,** Heard. **6,** Eddy. **7,** Teemed. **8,** Return. **13,** Cabinet. **15,** Earth. **16,** Remit. **18,** Bared. **19,** Eerie. **21,** Sac. **22,** Let. **24,** Assign. **25,** Turned. **27,** Pebble. **28,** Drudge. **30,** Weedy. **31,** Dined. **33,** Fret. **34,** Dude.

PUZZLE No. 153. Across: 3, Erect. **9,** Orange. **10,** Lariat. **11,** Ocean. **12,** Idea. **15,** List. **17,** Compass. **20,** Ate. **21,** Scrub. **23,** Real. **25,** Else. **26,** Ladle. **28,** Saw. **30,** Dresser. **33,** Anew. **35,** Tide. **36,** Rapid. **38,** Regret. **39,** Niggle. **40,** Paled. **Down: 1,** Tonic. **2,** Harem. **3,** Ego. **4,** Recess. **5,** Claw. **6,** Tan. **7,** Tibia. **8,** State. **13,** Doorman. **14,** Appal. **16,** Steered. **18,** Scold. **19,** Due. **22,** Blast. **24,** Lad. **27,** Ermine. **28,** Sabre. **29,** Wedge. **31,** Singe. **32,** Refer. **34,** Data. **36,** Rep. **37,** Did.

PUZZLE No. 154. Across: 1, Scribe. **5,** Stem. **8,** Sewer. **9,** Vat. **10,** Leer. **11,** Cure. **12,** Argue. **13,** Rocked. **16,** Firm. **18,** Even. **20,** Ant. **22,** Sue. **23,** Den. **24,** Alto. **25,** Pend. **28,** Totter. **30,** Fiend. **32,** Chic. **33,** Suit. **34,** Run. **35,** Lazed. **36,** Dull. **37,** Bridge. **Down: 1,** Severe. **2,** Reticent. **3,** Belief. **4,** Merriment. **5,** Secured. **6,** True. **7,** Meet. **8,** Sea. **14,** Dispensed. **15,** Men. **17,** Rue. **19,** Ventured. **20,** Alp. **21,** Topical. **26,** Doctor. **27,** Cringe. **29,** Acid. **30,** Fill. **31,** Dud.

PUZZLE No.155. Across: 1, Clash. **5,** Supple. **8,** Copse. **10,** Damage. **11,** Aped. **14,** Molest. **15,** Deceive. **18,** Tea. **19,** End. **21,** Dray. **23,** Error. **24,** Alas. **27,** Ton. **29,** Rag. **31,** Lantern. **32,** Driver. **34,** Date. **35,** Earned. **38,** Nudge. **39,** Talent. **40,** Edify. **Down: 2,** Lea. **3,** Scared. **4,** Hog. **5,** Seam. **6,** Peeled. **7,** Earthy. **9,** Pervert. **12,** Pot. **13,** Dear. **16,** Evil. **17,** Enrol. **20,** Donated. **22,** Aver. **24,** Ardent. **25,** Arid. **26,** Savage. **28,** Stored. **30,** Get. **33,** Rent. **36,** Age. **37,** Elf.

PUZZLE No.156. Across: 2, Actor. **7,** Oral. **8,** Unsure. **9,** Limit. **11,** Cur. **13,** Cad. **15,** Open. **16,** Cos. **18,** Fate. **19,** Deliver. **20,** Item. **22,** Ergo. **23,** Defence. **25,** Amen. **27,** Due. **28,** Here. **30,** Lid. **31,** Dud. **33,** Wedge. **36,** Debate. **37,** Need. **38,** Trend. **Down: 1,** Group. **2,** All. **3,** Tom. **4,** Rut. **5,** Ask. **6,** Great. **10,** Idol. **11,** Comical. **12,** Receded. **13,** Carried. **14,** Denoted. **16,** Ceded. **17,** Since. **18,** Fee. **21,** Men. **24,** Nude. **26,** Miner. **29,** Ruler. **32,** Bad. **33,** Wet. **34,** Die. **35,** End.

PUZZLE No.157. Across: 2, Start. **7,** State. **8,** Lemon. **10,** Enter. **12,** Car. **13,** Lined. **15,** Derided. **17,** Eroded. **19,** Lad. **20,** Dilated. **23,** Eyed. **25,** Done. **26,** Devised. **30,** Fad. **31,** Delete. **34,** Excited. **37,** Minor. **38,** Tan. **39,** Demon. **40,** Money. **41,** Teach. **42,** Steer. **Down: 1,** Stair. **2,** Steed. **3,** Tended. **4,** Rued. **5,** Decided. **6,** Bored. **9,** Mad. **11,** Relaxed. **13,** Lever. **14,** Noted. **16,** Rat. **18,** Divided. **21,** Dozen. **22,** Sewer. **24,** Defined. **27,** Vat. **28,** Demote. **29,** Extol. **32,** Liner. **33,** Torch. **35,** Can. **36,** Deft.

PUZZLE No.158. Across: 1, Part. **4,** Wit. **6,** Pick. **8,** Famous. **9,** Insane. **10,** Tap. **12,** Below. **14,** Sewed. **15,** Loose. **18,** Tender. **20,** Friend. **24,** Eaten. **26,** Sport. **28,** Dally. **30,** Fen. **32,** Favour. **33,** Enigma. **34,** Unit. **35,** Tot. **36,** Yarn. **Down: 2,** Amaze. **3,** Twofold. **4,** West. **5,** Trip. **6,** Paste. **7,** Concern. **11,** Ass. **12,** Bat. **13,** Woe. **16,** Ore. **17,** Eft. **19,** Explain. **21,** Red. **22,** Inanity. **23,** Dry. **25,** Ace. **27,** Roost. **29,** Lemur. **30,** Fret. **31,** Neat.

PUZZLE No.159. Across: 1, Torrid. **5,** Little. **8,** Pleasant. **9,** Rare. **10,** Odd. **12,** Dared. **15,** Pet. **17,** Err. **18,** Ill. **19,** Era. **20,** Eider. **21,** Aft. **22,** Log. **23,** Gun. **24,** Eat. **26,** Store. **29,** Ten. **33,** Stop. **34,** Subtract. **35,** Bridge. **36,** Tumble. **Down: 2,** Oiled. **3,** Rear. **4,** Drama. **5,** Lithe. **6,** Tire. **7,** Large. **10,** Obese. **11,** Dealt. **12,** Dregs. **13,** Radio. **14,** Dirge. **15,** Plant. **16,** Titan. **25,** Alter. **27,** Taste. **28,** Rebut. **30,** Excel. **31,** Sped. **32,** Grim.

PUZZLE No. 160. Across: 1, Grip. 4, Dip. 6, Cash. 9, Apt. 10, Conserve. 11, Bear. 14, Act. 16, Refer. 19, Disinter. 21, Tenet. 23, Dominate. 24, Tower. 27, Ran. 31, Mind. 33, Likeness. 34, Vie. 35, Weld. 36, Pad. 37, Side. **Down:** 2, Rook. 3, Pass. 4, Directed. 5, Peer. 6, Cable. 7, Ape. 8, Stale. 12, Admit. 13, Askew. 14, Ant. 15, Tenor. 17, Final. 18, Ripen. 20, Remarked. 22, Tin. 25, Olive. 26, Ended. 28, Slap. 29, Onus. 30, Used. 32, Nil.

PUZZLE No. 161. Across: 4, Porch. 7, Afresh. 9, Mat. 10, Pep. 12, Shape. 13, Oral. 15, Arise. 17, Dapper. 19, Raid. 20, Stair. 22, Sot. 24, Ripened. 27, Men. 28, Seamy. 31, Beat. 33, Stated. 35, Water. 37, Doll. 38, Panic. 39, Dip. 41, Nip. 42, Delete. 43, Ceded. **Down:** 1, Famous. 2, Armada. 3, Asp. 4, Pass. 5, Other. 6, Capsicum. 8, Heap. 11, Presented. 14, Lair. 16, Iron. 18, Prim. 21, Tolerate. 23, Test. 25, Pest. 26, Deed. 29, Adored. 30, Yelled. 32, Twine. 34, Arid. 36, Acid. 40, Pet.

PUZZLE No. 162. Across: 1, Recess. 5, Banana. 9, Eater. 10, Silent. 11, Gender. 12, Tibia. 14, Edam. 17, Nun. 18, Cure. 20, Dared. 22, Wired. 23, Ringlet. 24, Fetid. 26, Deter. 29, Edit. 30, Ten. 32, Dale. 33, Medal. 35, Ration. 36, Mortal. 37, Voter. 38, Dodder. 39, Depend. **Down:** 1, Rested. 2, Cellar. 3, Sent. 4, Satin. 5, Begin. 6, Area. 7, Ardour. 8, Agreed. 13, Bungled. 15, Dated. 16, Merit. 18, Cited. 19, Revel. 21, Did. 22, Wed. 24, Feared. 25, Tinted. 27, Tattle. 28, Reeled. 30, Tenor. 31, Named. 33, Move. 34, Lore.

PUZZLE No. 163. Across: 3, Later. 9, Animal. 10, Manage. 11, Plain. 12, Iris. 15, Lido. 17, Settled. 20, Den. 21, Ditch. 23, Oath. 25, Tale. 26, Eager. 28, Wee. 30, Desired. 33, Erne. 35, Tide. 36, Attic. 38, Grease. 39, Talent 40, Speed. **Down:** 1, Basis. 2, Limit. 3, Lap. 4, Allied. 5, Emit. 6, Ran. 7, Rapid. 8, Demon. 13, Recover. 14, State. 16, Deleted. 18, Dived. 19, Act. 22, Habit. 24, Had. 27, Recite. 28, Wedge. 29, Enter. 31, Rider. 32, Death. 34, Step. 36, Ass. 37, Cad.

PUZZLE No. 164. Across: 1, Madman. 5, Mule. 8, Women. 9, Din. 10, Lion. 11, Aide. 12, Event. 13, Summer. 16, Peer. 18, Eros. 20, Ate. 22, Set. 23, Red. 24, Mien. 25, Plea. 28, Dreamt. 30, Funny. 32, Tear. 33, Deaf. 34, Imp. 35, Tenet. 36, Rued. 37, Plunge. **Down:** 1, Modest. 2, Dynamite. 3, Asleep. 4, Converted. 5, Meander. 6, Unit. 7, Even. 8, Woe. 14, Responded. 15, Hod. 17, Eel. 19, Relation. 20, Aim. 21, Endured. 26, Artful. 27, Staple. 29, Stir. 30, Fate. 31, Yet.

PUZZLE No. 165. Across: 1, Canal. 5, Custom. 8, Serve. 10, Chaste. 11, Doom. 14, Errant. 15, Chamois. 18, Bed. 19, Net. 21, Dead. 23, Repel. 24, Chef. 27, Dim. 29, Wag. 31, Appoint. 32, Clever. 34, Rota. 35, Sodden. 38, Title. 39, Sparse. 40, Draft.- **Down:** 2, Ash. 3, Assume. 4, Let. 5, Cede. 6, Stored. 7, Minted. 9, Refined. 12, Orb. 13, Made. 16, Hush. 17, Sepia. 20, Tempest. 22, Akin. 24, Cactus. 25, Ewer. 26, Favour. 28, Ponder. 30, Get. 33, Rate. 36, Old. 37, Elf.

PUZZLE No. 166. Across: 2, Rigid. 7, Urge. 8, Outcry. 9, Doubt. 11, Imp. 13, Van. 15, Male. 16, Ram. 18, Bite. 19, Natural. 20, Gang. 22, Glut. 23, Noticed. 25, Need. 27, Did. 28, Diva. 30, End. 31, Nil. 33, Learn. 36, Future. 37, Emit. 38, Greet. **Down:** 1, Drama. 2, Red. 3, Gnu. 4, Dot. 5, Sty. 6, Great. 10, Beat. 11, Imagine. 12, Planned. 13, Villain. 14, Neutral. 16, Rapid. 17, Muted. 18, Bag. 21, God. 24, Cite. 26, Ensue. 29, Visit. 32, Mud. 33, Leg. 34, Ape. 35, Net.

PUZZLE No. 167. Across: 2, Pique. 7, Steam. 8, Debar. 10, Speed. 12, Lit. 13, Grate. 15, Debated. 17, Recede. 19, Fat. 20, Excited. 23, Prod. 25, Deft. 26, Refined. 30, Cur. 31, Deride. 34, Desired. 37, Petal. 38, Lad. 39, Droop. 40, Dated. 41, Sense. 42, Impel. **Down:** 1, Store. 2, Paste. 3, Impede. 4, Used. 5, Related. 6, Water. 9, Bit. 11, Defined. 13, Grope. 14, Actor. 16, Bat. 18, Expired. 21, Debit. 22, Steel. 24, Decided. 27, Fur. 28, Depose. 29, Delay. 32, Repel. 33, Daisy. 35, Sat. 36, Drum.

PUZZLE No. 168. Across: 1, Chic. 4, Cup. 6, Luck. 8, Furore. 9, Insane. 10, Wad. 12, Leant. 14, Bonus. 15, Eager. 18, Emerge. 20, United. 24, Tenet. 26, Using. 28, Weary. 30, Sup. 32, Bandit. 33, Learnt. 34, Cede. 35, Men. 36, Eyed. **Down:** 2, House. 3, Crooner. 4, Chew. 5, Paid. 6, Lasso. 7, Confuse. 11, Awe. 12, Lie. 13, Tag. 16, Get. 17, Run. 19, Mistake. 21, New. 22, Iterate. 23, Dry. 25, Emu. 27, Nudge. 29, Range. 30, Stem. 31, Plan.

PUZZLE No. 169. Across: 1, Gamble. 5, Strain. 8, Describe. 9, Dole. 10, Ate. 12, State. 15, Zoo. 17, Jot. 18, Axe. 19, Ode. 20, Under. 21, Ban. 22, Can. 23, Tor. 24, Tot. 26, Torch. 29, Ale. 33, Ship. 34, Exchange. 35, Bridge. 36, Expect. **Down:** 2, Alert. 3, Back. 4, Exist. 5, Sweet. 6, Rude. 7, Igloo. 10, About. 11, Eject. 12, Stunt. 13, Adder. 14, Earth. 15, Zebra. 16, Ounce. 25, Other. 27, Obese. 28, Cache. 30, Logic. 31, Sped. 32, Damp.

PUZZLE No. 170. Across: 1, Rash. 4, Cut. 6, Asti. 9, Fee. 10, Despised. 11, Tang. 14, Cod. 16, Greed. 19, Streamer. 21, Repay. 23, Rotating. 24, Yearn. 27, Tip. 31, Gulf. 33, Contract. 34, Lee. 35, Star. 36, Oil. 37, Mend. **Down:** 2, Apex. 3, Hope. 4, Customer. 5, Tidy. 6, After. 7, Sea. 8, Tense. 12, Essay. 13, Aroma. 14, Car. 15, Depot. 17, Eyrie. 18, Dodge. 20, Rational. 22, Yap. 25, Exult. 26, Refer. 28, Echo. 29, Grim. 30, Scan. 32, Lea.

PUZZLE No. 171. Across: 4, Issue. 7, Entire. 9, Ash. 10, Arc. 12, Legal. 13, Grow. 15, Novel. 17, Serene. 19, Load. 20, Title. 22, Fit. 24, Defiled. 27, Dad. 28, Needy. 31, Drab. 33, Rested. 35, Agent. 37, Dial. 38, State. 39, Tip. 41, Hat. 42, Recede. 43, Adder. **Down:** 1, Height. 2, Utmost. 3, Era. 4, Isle. 5, Shell. 6, Unabated. 8, Erne. 11, Confident. 14, Weld. 16, Veil. 18, Reed. 21, Iterated. 23, Tent. 25, Fare. 26, Deed. 29, Edited. 30, Yelled. 32, Bathe. 34, Stir. 36, Gear. 40, Pen.

PUZZLE No. 172. Across: 1, Peruse. 5, Statue. 9, Angle. 10, Salute. 11, Earned. 12, Ember. 14, Over. 17, Yap. 18, Rear. 20, Rider. 22, Badge. 23, Benefit. 24, Steed. 26, Beret. 29, Tall. 30, Rut. 32, Deer. 33, Oiled. 35, Acting. 36, Pardon. 37, Civil. 38, Dodged. 39, Decree. **Down:** 1, Pastor. 2, Rolled. 3, Sate. 4, Enemy. 5, Sleep. 6, Tear. 7, Tended. 8, Endure. 13, Baleful. 15, Vista. 16, Rebel. 18, Rated. 19, Agree. 21, Red. 22, Bib. 24, Strand. 25, Elated. 27, Render. 28, Trance. 30, Rigid. 31, Tepid. 33, Once. 34, Dale.

PUZZLE No. 173. Across: 3, Taste. 9, Ironed. 10, Offend. 11, Event. 12, Area. 15, Keep. 17, Convent. 20, Rat. 21, Tired. 23, Avid. 25, Deal. 26, Drain. 28, Act. 30, Deleted. 33, Deem. 35, Rare. 36, Sight. 38, Recoup. 39, Ermine. 40, Merry. **Down:** 1, Lilac. 2, Token. 3, Tee. 4, Advent. 5, Tone. 6, Eft. 7, Refer. 8, Adept. 13, Romance. 14, Avoid. 16, Earlier. 18, Timid. 19, Wed. 22, Defer. 24, Dry. 27, Nether. 28, Adore. 29, Teach. 31, Tacit. 32, Deter. 34, Ripe. 36, Sum. 37, Try.

PUZZLE No. 174. Across: 1, Albeit. 5, Ooze. 8, Sharp. 9, Ill. 10, Flea. 11, Dear. 12, Aspen. 13, Retard. 16, Mere. 18, Edam. 20, Old. 22, Can. 23, Den. 24, Tier. 25, Ewer. 28, Devote. 30, Spite. 32, Trip. 33, Fair. 34, Aft. 35, Debut. 36, Died. 37, Adhere. **Down:** 1, Aviary. 2, Belittle. 3, Infirm. 4, Chastened. 5, Ordered. 6, Open. 7, Earl. 8, Sea. 14, Deceitful. 15, Tan. 17, Raw. 19, Decorate. 20, Oil. 21, Dropped. 26, Reared. 27, Fettle. 29, Stud. 30, Side. 31, Eat.

PUZZLE No. 175. Across: 1, Crypt. 5, Basked. 8, Lodge. 10, Severe. 11, Aped. 14, Remark. 15, Plastic. 18, Get. 19, Nod. 21, Debt. 23, Demon. 24, Step. 27, Din. 29, Vat. 31, Careful. 32, Soiled. 34, Lane. 35, Elicit. 38, Faded. 39, Modest. 40, Tenet. **Down:** 2, Roe. 3, Please. 4, Tor. 5, Bear. 6, Seemed. 7, Docket. 9, Defined. 12, Peg. 13, Date. 16, Lift. 17, Comic. 20, Donated. 22, Beau. 24, System. 25, Evil. 26, Palate. 28, Decide. 30, Ten. 33, Deft. 36, Let. 37, Ire.

PUZZLE No. 176. Across: 2, Grasp. 7, Rota. 8, Astute. 9, Petty. 11, Cow. 13, Rid. 15, Oral. 16, Vat. 18, Mere. 19, Married. 20, Item. 22, Tune. 23, Natural. 25, Aver. 27, Eat. 28, Zero. 30, Lid. 31, Dip. 33, Blind. 36, Stride. 37, Unit. 38, Theme. **Down:** 1, Motor. 2, Gap. 3, Aft. 4, Pay. 5, Sty. 6, Stair. 10, Tear. 11, Comical. 12, Wakened. 13, Reduced. 14, Develop. 16, Vague. 17, Treat. 18, Met. 21, Mar. 24, Rail. 26, Vista. 29, Rigid. 32, Win. 33, Bet. 34, Ire. 35, Due.

PUZZLE No. 177. Across: 2, Spill. 7, Ruler. 8, Sewer. 10, Voter. 12, Par. 13, Grief. 15, Secured. 17, Horrid. 19, Cat. 20, Towered. 23, Site. 25, Deal. 26, Engaged. 30, Cot. 31, Demote. 34, Piloted. 37, Money. 38, Mad. 39, Demur. 40, Rider. 41, Rapid. 42, Creel. **Down:** 1, Burro. 2, Sever. 3, Profit. 4, Lees. 5, Reputed. 6, Beret. 9, War. 11, Receded. 13, Ghost. 14, Irate. 16, Car. 18, Donated. 21, Demon. 22, Alley. 24, Encoded. 27, Got. 28, Demure. 29, Limit. 32, Moral. 33, Tepid. 35, Lad. 36, Dear.

PUZZLE No. 178. Across: 1, Chic. 4, Fad. 6, Dupe. 8, Dismal. 9, Nation. 10, Lay. 12, Stool. 14, Brain. 15, Ready. 18, Poster. 20, Elated. 24, Total. 26, Since. 28, Glade. 30, End. 32, Sinned. 33, Reward. 34, Yell. 35, Map. 36, Deep. **Down:** 2, Hoist. 3, Comfort. 4, Fell. 5, Deny. 6, Deter. 7, Promise. 11, Aid. 12, Sip. 13, Lee. 16, Art. 17, Yet. 19, Orifice. 21, Lag. 22, Allowed. 23, Die. 25, Own. 27, Canal. 29, Dirge. 30, Edam. 31, Drip.

PUZZLE No. 179. Across: 1, Garret. 5, Gather. 8, Comprise. 9, Rout. 10, Sad. 12, Stamp. 15, Set. 17, Elk. 18, Ilk. 19, Ill. 20, Image. 21, Ass. 22, All. 23, Cut. 24, Try. 26, Lodge. 29, Eye. 33, Mute. 34, Deadened. 35, Tender. 36, Tirade. **Down:** 2, Aroma. 3, Ripe. 4, Twist. 5, Gleam. 6, Tire. 7, Exude. 10, Swift. 11, Delay. 12, Skill. 13, Award. 14, Piece. 15, Skate. 16, Taste. 25, Rouse. 27, Order. 28, Grant. 30, Yield. 31, Send. 32, Beer.

PUZZLE No. 180. Across: 1, Clap. 4, Imp. 6, Arid. 9, Van. 10, Interval. 11, Once. 14, Ant. 16, Adore. 19, Accepted. 21, Tenet. 23, Domicile. 24, Every. 27, Roe. 31, Fret. 33, Alienate. 34, See. 35, Weld. 36, Sin. 37, Part. **Down:** 2, Line. 3, Peel. 4, Invented. 5, Pull. 6, Avoid. 7, Ran. 8, Incur. 12, Badge. 13, Scene. 14, Apt. 15, Tenor. 17, Oasis. 18, Expel. 20, Demotion. 22, Tie. 25, Verse. 26, Rated. 28, Mass. 29, Snap. 30, Stir. 32, Eel.

PUZZLE No. 181. Across: 4, Block. 7, Streak. 9, Ore. 10, Rid. 12, Avert. 13, Edam. 15, Wedge. 17, Defile. 19, Lull. 20, Plane. 22, Elm. 24, Dangled. 27, Tea. 28, Roost. 31, Aged. 33, Attend. 35, Water. 37, Edit. 38, Rider. 39, Dip. 41, Lid. 42, Mettle. 43, Child. **Down:** 1, Asleep. 2, Armada. 3, Oar. 4, Brag. 5, Level. 6, Careless. 8, Kiwi. 11, Delegated. 14, Mend. 16, Dell. 18, Feat. 21, Languish. 23, Mere. 25, Neat. 26, Done. 29, Oddity. 30, Totter. 32, Dwell. 34, Trim. 36, Arid. 40, Pet.

PUZZLE No. 182. Across: 1, Stench. 5, Statue. 9, Haste. 10, Defeat. 11, Oafish. 12, Recur. 14, Tarn. 17, Dot. 18, Cede. 20, Enter. 22, Jaded. 23, Earthen. 24, Seedy. 26, Tamed. 29, Tray. 30, Age. 32, Lure. 33, Trend. 35, Ponder. 36, Differ. 37, Laden. 38, Rudely. 39, Delete. **Down:** 1, Sedate. 2, Effort. 3, Char. 4, Hated. 5, Stout. 6, Tear. 7, Tailed. 8, Echoed. 13, Cottage. 15, Anger. 16, Needy. 18, Canal. 19, Defer. 21, Ray. 22, Jet. 24, Stupor. 25, Earned. 27, Muffle. 28, Decree. 30, Array. 31, Ended. 33, Tell. 34, Dine.

PUZZLE No. 183. Across: 3, Tease. 9, Retain. 10, Enfold. 11, Paced. 12, Acid. 15, Oral. 17, Monocle. 20, Ale. 21, Expel. 23, Fool. 25, Menu. 26, Roved. 28, Ass. 30, Lowered. 33, Used. 35, Ride. 36, Avoid. 38, Unsure. 39, Latent. 40, Tried. **Down:** 1, Dream. 2, Stain. 3, Tip. 4, Enable. 5, Seed. 6, End. 7, Cobra. 8, Addle. 13, Confess. 14, Donor. 16, Alluded. 18, Excel. 19, Hem. 22, Lever. 24, Lot. 27, Docile. 28, Augur. 29, Sense. 31, River. 32, Death. 34, Aver. 36, Art 37, **Dad.**

PUZZLE No. 184. Across: 1, Modern. 5, Away. 8, Force. 9, Tar. 10, Lion. 11, Claw. 12, Edged. 13, Ensued. 16, Film. 18, Else. 20, Cos. 22, Van. 23, Die. 24, Cant. 25, Eyed. 28, Decent. 30, Crass. 32, Plot. 33, Item. 34, Asp. 35, Decoy. 36, Need. 37, Adhere. **Down:** 1, Matter. 2, Derision. 3, Relief. 4, Condemned. 5, Acceded. 6, Weld. 7, Yawn. 8, Foe. 14, Diversion. 15, Use. 17, Lay. 19, Liberate. 20, Can. 21, Started. 26, Deemed. 27, Staple. 29, Open. 30, Code. 31, Sty.

PUZZLE No. 185. Across: 1, Bogus. 5, Tussle. 8, Nudge. 10, Sender. 11, Stay. 14, Talent. 15, Frantic. 18, Pea. 19, Nag. 21, Dray. 23, Repel. 24, Herd. 27, Den. 29, Eel. 31, Reverse. 32, Dismal. 34, Taxi. 35, Adroit. 38, Value. 39, Needle. 40, Erred. **Down:** 2, Ode. 3, Undone. 4, Sue. 5, Test. 6, Scaled. 7, Earthy. 9, Drained. 12, Tap. 13, Year. 16, Role. 17, Caper. 20, General. 22, Alas. 24, Hidden. 25, Rest. 26, Demand. 28, Bearer. 30, Lax. 33, Live. 36, Due. 37, Ire.

PUZZLE No. 186. Across: 2, Creel. 7, Zero. 8, Excite. 9, Dealt. 11, Ave. 13, Mud. 15, Tent. 16, Tee. 18, Gate. 19, Mission. 20, Laid. 22, Taxi. 23, Capital. 25, Eyed. 27, Day. 28, Mere. 30, Red. 31, Did. 33, Terse. 36, Cringe. 37, Wail. 38, Nudge. **Down:** 1, Delve. 2, Cod. 3, Era. 4, Let. 5, Act. 6, Stout. 10, Lees. 11, Atelier. 12, Enticed. 13, Managed. 14, Desired. 16, Timid. 17, Essay. 18, Got. 21, Dad. 24, Tame. 26, Yearn. 29, Rigid. 32, Ink. 33, Ten. 34, Rid. 35, Ewe.

PUZZLE No. 187. Across: 2, Range. 7, Hades. 8, Pilot. 10, Allow. 12, Now. 13, Dance. 15, Damaged. 17, Elated. 19, Van. 20, Potency. 23, Iced. 25, Earl. 26, Dilated. 30, Sit. 31, Dashed. 34, Misdeed. 37, Mitre. 38, Lea. 39, Divan. 40, Claim. 41, Screw. 42, Stake. **Down:** 1, Banal. 2, React. 3, Asleep. 4, Good. 5, Finance. 6, Cowed. 9, Log. 11, Wavered. 13, Devil. 14, Naked. 16, Man. 18, Donated. 21, Yacht. 22, Elude. 24, Disdain. 27, Lie. 28, Damask. 29, Silly. 32, Since. 33, Erred. 35, Sea. 36, Diet.

PUZZLE No. 188. Across: 1, Ramp. 4, Bun. 6, Pick. 8, Pirate. 9, Animal. 10, Rot. 12, Gusto. 14, Depot. 15, Inane. 18, Placed. 20, Nature. 24, Dodge. 26, Unite. 28, Edict. 30, Eft. 32, Demand. 33, Erotic. 34, Step. 35, Mum. 36, Sham. **Down:** 2, Adieu. 3, Plastic. 4, Beer. 5, Neat. 6, Price. 7, Clamour. 11, Own. 12, Gap. 13, One. 16, Add. 17, End. 19, Lenient. 21, Age. 22, Tedious. 23, Eat. 25, Oaf. 27, Tramp. 29, China. 30, Edam. 31, Team.

PUZZLE No. 189. Across: 1, Recess. 5, Escape. 8, Prospect. 9, Slap. 10, Aye. 12, Dream. 15, Fat. 17, Awe. 18, Ill. 19, Sot. 20, Mined. 21, Ire. 22, Ego. 23, Gun. 24, Tin. 26, Noise. 29, God. 33, Used. 34, Headland. 35, Teeter. 36, Expert. **Down:** 2, Early. 3, East. 4, Steer. 5, Extra. 6, Cost. 7, Plaza. 10, Asset. 11, Eaten. 12, Demon. 13, Ennui. 14, Midge. 15, Fling. 16, Tread. 25, Issue. 27, Other. 28, Stale. 30, Owner. 31, Edit. 32, Clap.

PUZZLE No. 190. Across: 1, Fret. 4, Cot. 6, Cask. 9, Hit. 10, Consumed. 11, Alas. 14, Eel. 16, Start. 19, Reporter. 21, Revel. 23, Demanded. 24, Sweet. 27, Ray. 31, Sift. 33, Constant. 34, Too. 35, Feel. 36, Dud. 37, Pipe. **Down:** 2, Rook. 3, Test. 4, Competed. 5, Tidy. 6, Chart. 7, Ail. 8, Stair. 12, Dross. 13, Spate. 14, Err. 15, Lever. 17, Abide. 18, Trade. 20, Remained. 22, Lay. 25, Write. 26, Extol. 28, Acid. 29, Stop. 30, Snap. 32, Foe.

PUZZLE No. 191. Across: 4, False. 7, Ocelot. 9, Old. 10, Tor. 12, Edged. 13, Mood. 15, Rebel. 17, Trance. 19, Each. 20, Dream. 22, Lad. 24, Besides. 27, Nun. 28, Seedy. 31, Rota. 33, Risked. 35, Scene. 37, Kill. 38, Quota. 39, Gel. 41, Elk. 42, Recede. 43, Pearl. **Down:** 1, Formed. 2, Demote. 3, Hot. 4, Flee. 5, Addle. 6, Sketched. 8, Torn. 11, Reclining. 14, Drab. 16, Bead. 18, Amen. 21, Resolute. 23, Desk. 25, Sure. 26, Seek. 29, Edited. 30, Yelled. 32, Aster. 34, Seer. 36, Call. 40, Leg.

PUZZLE No. 192. Across: 1, Portal. **5,** Acumen. **9,** Pitch. **10,** Rotten. **11,** Tailed. **12,** Deter. **14,** Sore. **17,** Did. **18,** Here. **20,** Event. **22,** Waded. **23,** Tangled. **24,** Order. **26,** Beret. **29,** Stir. **30,** Met. **32,** Sole. **33,** Faded. **35,** Limpid. **36,** Nickel. **37,** Lager. **38,** Redeem. **39,** Teeter. **Down: 1,** Peruse. **2,** Retire. **3,** Aped. **4,** Lined. **5,** Acted. **6,** Char. **7,** Melted. **8,** Nudged. **13,** Tingled. **15,** Overt. **16,** Enter. **18,** Hades. **19,** Revel. **21,** Tar. **22,** Web. **24,** Ostler. **25,** Dimmed. **27,** Rocket. **28,** Teller. **30,** Madam. **31,** Tenet. **33,** File. **34,** Dire.

PUZZLE No. 193. Across: 3, State. **9,** Leader. **10,** Erotic. **11,** Water. **12,** Open. **15,** Till. **17,** Managed. **20,** Rue. **21,** Ruler. **23,** Tied. **25,** Wing. **26,** Dozen. **28,** Fad. **30,** Tidings. **33,** Ilex. **35,** Duet. **36,** Doubt. **38,** Studio. **39,** Lugger. **40,** Green. **Down: 1,** Gloom. **2,** Haven. **3,** Sew. **4,** Trader. **5,** Teem. **6,** Err. **7,** Stair. **8,** Scale. **13,** Partial. **14,** Named. **16,** Luggage. **18,** Duvet. **19,** Hew. **22,** Rigid. **24,** Dog. **27,** Nimble. **28,** First. **29,** Debut. **31,** Nudge. **32,** Start. **34,** Door. **36,** Dig. **37,** Tun.

PUZZLE No. 194. Across: 1, Resist. **5,** Deem. **8,** Muted. **9,** See. **10,** Neat. **11,** Cite. **12,** Pilot. **13,** Relief. **16,** Data. **18,** Emit. **20,** End. **22,** Sot. **23,** Dam. **24,** Rage. **25,** Twee. **28,** Drench. **30,** Arena. **32,** Cube. **33,** Iced. **34,** Tip. **35,** Leant. **36,** Eyed. **37,** Educed. **Down: 1,** Resort. **2,** Sterling. **3,** Sinned. **4,** Mutilated. **5,** Decoded. **6,** Edit. **7,** Meet. **8,** Map. **14,** Fastening. **15,** Dim. **17,** Tow. **19,** Magnetic. **20,** Ear. **21,** Decreed. **26,** Eroded. **27,** Shaped. **29,** Ache. **30,** Able. **31,** Act.

PUZZLE No. 195. Across: 1, Pleat. **5,** Dispel. **8,** Swine. **10,** Wanton. **11,** Epic. **14,** Devote. **15,** Contend. **18,** Red. **19,** Eat. **21,** Rest. **23,** Alter. **24,** Weld. **27,** Yet. **29,** Eel. **31,** Daunted. **32,** Dinner. **34,** Tide. **35,** Unison. **38,** Asset. **39,** Dodder. **40,** Weary. **Down: 2,** Lea. **3,** Astute. **4,** Two. **5,** Deed. **6,** Sliver. **7,** Latent. **9,** Inanely. **12,** Per. **13,** Code. **16,** Once. **17,** Dated. **20,** Tetanus. **22,** Sane. **24,** Wedged. **25,** Lent. **26,** Denied. **28,** Invite. **30,** Led. **33,** Rear. **36,** New. **37,** Oar.

PUZZLE No. 196. Across: 2, Erect. **7,** Stub. **8,** Impair. **9,** Brute. **11,** Did. **13,** Rid. **15,** Eden. **16,** Sip. **18,** Wear. **19,** Stormed. **20,** Role. **22,** Dump. **23,** Instant. **25,** Send. **27,** Elk. **28,** Fete. **30,** See. **31,** Dud. **33,** Comic. **36,** Cinema. **37,** Unit. **38,** Noble. **Down: 1,** Staid. **2,** Ebb. **3,** Emu. **4,** Tie. **5,** Apt. **6,** Tibia. **10,** Trio. **11,** Depress. **12,** Decline. **13,** Reduced. **14,** Dropped. **16,** State. **17,** Prank. **18,** Wed. **21,** End. **24,** Also. **26,** Eerie. **29,** Tunic. **32,** Set. **33,** Can. **34,** Mob. **35,** Cue.

PUZZLE No. 197. Across: 2, Asked. **7,** Globe. **8,** Adore. **10,** Avail. **12,** Awe. **13,** Grate. **15,** Toppled. **17,** Revere. **19,** Wet. **20,** Entered. **23,** Said. **25,** Dire. **26,** Deliver. **30,** Lac. **31,** Decide. **34,** Scraped. **37,** Cited. **38,** Toy. **39,** Dazed. **40,** Cower. **41,** Death. **42,** Steer. **Down: 1,** Flare. **2,** Abate. **3,** Severe. **4,** Emit. **5,** Adapted. **6,** Greet. **9,** Owl. **11,** Lowered. **13,** Grasp. **14,** Avoid. **16,** Per. **18,** Enticed. **21,** Digit. **22,** Sewed. **24,** Delayed. **27,** Lap. **28,** Recede. **29,** Actor. **32,** Cider. **33,** Deity. **35,** Row. **36,** Dart.

PUZZLE No. 198. Across: 1, Wide. **4,** Mud. **6,** Rite. **8,** Blithe. **9,** Avidly. **10,** Tag. **12,** Coral. **14,** Tepid. **15,** Ceded. **18,** Settee. **20,** Orange. **24,** Noted. **26,** Spray. **28,** Doubt. **30,** Off. **32,** Tender. **33,** Return. **34,** Used. **35,** Lay. **36,** Drew. **Down: 2,** Igloo. **3,** Extract. **4,** Meet. **5,** Drag. **6,** Raise. **7,** Telling. **11,** Ape. **12,** Cos. **13,** Lee. **16,** Den. **17,** Dot. **19,** Express. **21,** Red. **22,** Adopted. **23,** Eft. **25,** Oaf. **27,** Aided. **29,** Barge. **30,** Oral. **31,** Fray.

PUZZLE No. 199, Across: 1, Cancel. **5,** Perish. **8,** Pretence. **9,** Sink. **10,** Hem. **12,** Chest. **15,** Let. **17,** Ash. **18,** Ewe. **19,** Inn. **20,** Image. **21,** All. **22,** Ire. **23,** Tan. **24,** Tea. **26,** Fresh. **29,** Try. **33,** Ache. **34,** Detonate. **35,** Pledge. **36,** Despot. **Down: 2,** Agree. **3,** Cite. **4,** Lunch. **5,** Press. **6,** Risk. **7,** Since. **10,** Hoist. **11,** Mania. **12,** Chief. **13,** Erase. **14,** Teeth. **15,** Leant. **16,** Tally. **25,** Excel. **27,** Ridge. **28,** Sited. **30,** Ratio. **31,** Mend. **32,** Onus.

PUZZLE No. 200. Across: 1, Idol. **4,** Art. **6,** Cram. **9,** Low. **10,** Confused. **11,** Edam. **14,** And. **16,** Greed. **19,** Deserted. **21,** Metal. **23,** Demanded. **24,** Total. **27,** Rag. **31,** Shoe. **33,** Original. **34,** Err. **35,** Fret. **36,** Dog. **37,** Deem. **Down: 2,** Door. **3,** Lift. **4,** Assented. **5,** Tidy. **6,** Clear. **7,** Rod. **8,** Awake. **12,** Admit. **13,** Asset. **14,** Arm. **15,** Deter. **17,** Elude. **18,** Dandy. **20,** Damaging. **22,** Lag. **25,** Other. **26,** Avert. **28,** Cold. **29,** Mind. **30,** Wane. **32,** Ore

PUZZLE No. 201. Across: 4, Kiosk. **7,** Resort. **9,** Sin. **10,** Cos. **12,** Waved. **13,** Wood. **15,** Resin. **17,** Repent. **19,** Emit. **20,** Hotel. **22,** Sup. **24,** Receded. **27,** Ail. **28,** React. **31,** Drew. **33,** Tested. **35,** Obese. **37,** Done. **38,** Seamy. **39,** Sap. **41,** Era. **42,** Talent. **43,** Prone. **Down: 1,** Growth. **2,** Escort. **3,** Arc. **4,** Kiwi. **5,** Inane. **6,** Specific. **8,** Tore. **11,** Senseless. **14,** Deer. **16,** Stud. **18,** Plea. **21,** Overseer. **23,** Pert. **25,** Cite. **26,** Deed. **29,** Adored. **30,** Treaty. **32,** Women. **34,** Seat. **36,** Byre. **40,** Pay.

PUZZLE No. 202. Across: 1, Dogged. **5,** Scarab. **9,** Reach. **10,** Banana. **11,** Raider. **12,** Elder. **14,** Tale. **17,** Tow. **18,** Mere. **20,** Event. **22,** Lemon. **23,** Rotated. **24,** Pilot. **26,** Tacit. **29,** Idol. **30,** Sew. **32,** Lane. **33,** Coded. **35,** Kennel. **36,** Dipped. **37,** Dirge. **38,** Dodged. **39,** Editor. **Down: 1,** Debate. **2,** Gentle. **3,** Erne. **4,** Dealt. **5,** Screw. **6,** Char. **7,** Redeem. **8,** Barren. **13,** Donated. **15,** Avoid. **16,** Enrol. **18,** Medal. **19,** Robin. **21,** Tot. **22,** Let. **24,** Picked. **25,** Loaned. **27,** Carpet. **28,** Tender. **30,** Solid. **31,** Wedge. **33,** Cede. **34,** Died.

PUZZLE No. 203. Across: 3, Attic. **9,** Retire. **10,** Rushed. **11,** Tenor. **12,** Evil. **15,** Pace. **17,** Reduced. **20,** For. **21,** River. **23,** Even. **25,** Gist. **26,** Dated. **28,** Gas. **30,** Deficit. **33,** Once. **35,** Dune. **36,** Limit. **38,** Sandal. **39,** Native. **40,** Dozen. **Down: 1,** Order. **2,** Staid. **3,** Art. **4,** Teeter. **5,** Iron. **6,** Cur. **7,** Sheaf. **8,** Adder. **13,** Veteran. **14,** Lured. **16,** Contain. **18,** Dived. **19,** Peg. **22,** Rigid. **24,** Nag. **27,** Define. **28,** Gorse. **29,** Scene. **31,** Cupid. **32,** Tenet. **34,** Silo. **36,** Lad. **37,** Tan.

PUZZLE No. 204. Across: 1, Defect. **5,** Dawn. **8,** Sober. **9,** Mum. **10,** Slur. **11,** Lift. **12,** Embed. **13,** Teller. **16,** Tern. **18,** Eden. **20,** Car. **22,** Mat. **23,** Dim. **24,** Bare. **25,** Aped. **28,** Dispel. **30,** Meant. **32,** Read. **33,** Doom. **34,** Rag. **35,** Deter. **36,** Seed. **37,** Fluent. **Down: 1,** Demote. **2,** Familiar. **3,** Cosset. **4,** Tormented. **5,** Deleted. **6,** Arid. **7,** Note. **8,** Sue. **14,** Remainder. **15,** Hem. **17,** Rap. **19,** Disperse. **20,** Can. **21,** Receded. **26,** Dismal. **27,** Flight. **29,** Eros. **30,** Made. **31,** Tor.

PUZZLE No. 205. Across: 1, Lasso. **5,** Sagged. **8,** Arena. **10,** Stolen. **11,** Lash. **14,** Expose. **15,** Fearful. **18,** Eel. **19,** Ram. **21,** Dead. **23,** Petal. **24,** Debt. **27,** Den. **29,** Aid. **31,** Rallied. **32,** Barrow. **34,** Dine. **35,** Eloped. **38,** Laden. **39,** Slight. **40,** Edged. **Down: 2,** Apt. **3,** Salary. **4,** Ore. **5,** Sale. **6,** Gasped. **7,** Depend. **9,** Endured. **12,** Axe. **13,** Hole. **16,** Ease. **17,** Later. **20,** Managed. **22,** Acme. **24,** Debris. **25,** Bard. **26,** Tiring. **28,** Almond. **30,** Don. **33,** Welt. **36,** Lee. **37,** Eye.

PUZZLE No. 206. Across: 2, Order. **7,** Tiff. **8,** Astern. **9,** Fiery. **11,** Dim. **13,** Dam. **15,** Edam. **16,** Hem. **18,** Bite. **19,** Tedious. **20,** Cram. **22,** Stun. **23,** Galleon. **25,** Need. **27,** Oar. **28,** Bran. **30,** Did. **31,** Big. **33,** Snout. **36,** Recede. **37,** Item. **38,** Wedge. **Down: 1,** Rigid. **2,** Off. **3,** Due. **4,** Ray. **5,** Sty. **6,** Treat. **10,** Rued. **11,** Descend. **12,** Managed. **13,** Disturb. **14,** Meaning. **16,** Hello. **17,** Minor. **18,** Bus. **21,** Mad. **24,** Earn. **26,** Eider. **29,** Aimed. **32,** Wet. **33,** Sew. **34,** Old. **35,** Tie.

PUZZLE No. 207. Across: 2, Crisp. **7,** Genre. **8,** Demur. **10,** Enter. **12,** Cat. **13,** Beret. **15,** Merited. **17,** Reeled. **19,** Lad. **20,** Dilated. **23,** Seed. **25,** Dear. **26,** Resided. **30,** Bad. **31,** Desire. **34,** Decayed. **37,** Famed. **38,** Pot. **39,** Dozed. **40,** Sewer. **41,** Alter. **42,** Petty. **Down: 1,** Levee. **2,** Creel. **3,** Rented. **4,** Stem. **5,** Decided. **6,** Muted. **9,** Mat. **11,** Relaxed. **13,** Brash. **14,** Refer. **16,** Rat. **18,** Divided. **21,** Denim. **22,** Breed. **24,** Debated. **27,** Say. **28,** Defeat. **29,** Repel. **32,** Sadly. **33,** Rebel. **35,** Cow. **36,** Done.

PUZZLE No. 208. Across: 1, Core. **4,** Mug. **6,** Type. **8,** Aspect. **9,** Outlet. **10,** Had. **12,** Steal. **14,** Lever. **15,** Terse. **18,** Allege. **20,** Earned. **24,** Delve. **26,** Sneer. **28,** Ended. **30,** Wed. **32,** Future. **33,** Reward. **34,** Edit. **35,** Dog. **36,** Duty. **Down: 2,** Onset. **3,** Elevate. **4,** Myth. **5,** Good. **6,** Title. **7,** Precede. **11,** Ass. **12,** Sea. **13,** Leg. **16,** Red. **17,** Eel. **19,** Languid. **21,** Ave. **22,** Renewed. **23,** Dud. **25,** Eke. **27,** Erupt. **29,** Egret. **30,** Weld. **31,** Drag.

PUZZLE No. 209. Across: 1, Decent. **5,** Letter. **8,** Consumed. **9,** Away. **10,** Set. **12,** Adder. **15,** Let. **17,** Rug. **18,** Use. **19,** Spa. **20,** Extol. **21,** Van. **22,** Men. **23,** Eye. **24,** Lap. **26,** Tired. **29,** Lie. **33,** Curt. **34,** Terrible. **35,** Keeper. **36,** Hallow. **Down: 2,** Evoke. **3,** Ease. **4,** Tamed. **5,** Lodge. **6,** Team. **7,** Erase. **10,** Sisal. **11,** Tramp. **12,** Agent. **13,** Deter. **14,** Ruled. **15,** Level. **16,** Tense. **25,** Acute. **27,** Inter. **28,** Earth. **30,** Igloo. **31,** Stop. **32,** Till.

PUZZLE No. 210. Across: 1, Oral. **4,** Pen. **6,** Tape. **9,** Era. **10,** Prospect. **11,** Acne. **14,** Fat. **16,** React. **19,** Acquired. **21,** Tenor. **23,** Demurred. **24,** Debar. **27,** Tin. **31,** Grid. **33,** Pristine. **34,** Ore. **35,** Bred. **36,** Rue. **37,** Yank. **Down: 2,** Rare. **3,** Last. **4,** Prepared. **5,** Note. **6,** Tease. **7,** Arc. **8,** Panic. **12,** Saved. **13,** Squib. **14,** Fit. **15,** Tenet. **17,** Adore. **18,** Trade. **20,** Domicile. **22,** Run. **25,** Error. **26,** Added. **28,** Spar. **29,** Stay. **30,** Anon. **32,** Ire.

PUZZLE No. 211. Across: 4, First. **7,** Rioted. **9,** Fan. **10,** Bad. **12,** Inane. **13,** Step. **15,** Title. **17,** Grease. **19,** Rout. **20,** Stood. **22,** Pry. **24,** Defamed. **27,** Nor. **28,** Learn. **31,** Diva. **33,** Wallet. **35,** Bulge. **37,** Role. **38,** Talon. **39,** Eat. **41,** Vim. **42,** Novice. **43,** Beret. **Down: 1,** Crisis. **2,** Forego. **3,** Web. **4,** Fail. **5,** Inner. **6,** Singular. **8,** Data. **11,** Disparage. **14,** Prod. **16,** Term. **18,** Eden. **21,** Titivate. **23,** Yell. **25,** Fowl. **26,** Deer. **29,** Atomic. **30,** Needed. **32,** Above. **34,** Lean. **36,** Unit. **40,** Top.

PUZZLE No. 212. Across: 1, Recess. **5,** Asleep. **9,** April. **10,** Muddle. **11,** Middle. **12,** Tamed. **14,** Sale. **17,** Rid. **18,** Rate. **20,** Steam. **22,** Wired. **23,** Tangled. **24,** Miser. **26,** Debit. **29,** Icon. **30,** Bed. **32,** Rude. **33,** Model. **35,** Reason. **36,** Torpor. **37,** Defer. **38,** Reeled. **39,** Reader. **Down: 1,** Remiss. **2,** Coddle. **3,** Salt. **4,** Spear. **5,** Aimed. **6,** Slid. **7,** Endear. **8,** Peeled. **13,** Mingled. **15,** Attic. **16,** Eaten. **18,** Rider. **19,** Tepid. **21,** Mar. **22,** Wed. **24,** Mirror. **25,** Solace. **27,** Bumped. **28,** Terror. **30,** Boned. **31,** Deter. **33,** Mode. **34,** Lore.

PUZZLE No. 213. Across: 3, Taboo. **9,** Letter. **10,** Barren. **11,** Actor. **12,** Aped. **15,** Once. **17,** Married. **20,** God. **21,** Rapid. **23,** Dear. **25,** Mien. **26,** Moved. **28,** Leg. **30,** Defence. **33,** Idol. **35,** Rota. **36,** Bogus. **38,** Hugged. **39,** Revere. **40,** Tenet. **Down: 1,** Gleam. **2,** Steer. **3,** Tea. **4,** Archer. **5,** Oboe. **6,** Oar. **7,** Bring. **8,** Ended. **13,** Paddled. **14,** Dream. **16,** Connect. **18,** Dated. **19,** Dim. **22,** Diner. **24,** Rob. **27,** Demure. **28,** Lithe. **29,** Gorge. **31,** Noted. **32,** Eased. **34,** Rode. **36,** Bet. **37,** Set.

PUZZLE No. 214. Across: 1, Endure. **5,** Hunt. **8,** Sewer. **9,** Bar. **10,** Beer. **11,** Ague. **12,** Amble. **13,** Danger. **16,** Sect. **18,** Head. **20,** Led. **22,** Tot. **23,** Yap. **24,** Side. **25,** Used. **28,** Dahlia. **30,** Borne. **32,** Nous. **33,** Inch. **34,** Eel. **35,** Fiend. **36,** Tuft. **37,** Edited. **Down: 1,** Embody. **2,** Deranged. **3,** Rabies. **4,** Permitted. **5,** Healthy. **6,** Urge. **7,** Teem. **8,** Sea. **14,** Returning. **15,** Tap. **17,** Cos. **19,** Earliest. **20,** Lit. **21,** Deposit. **26,** Dashed. **27,** Pallid. **29,** Knit. **30,** Buff. **31,** End.

PUZZLE No. 215. Across: 1, Leapt. **5,** Strain. **8,** Revel. **10,** Define. **11,** Iron. **14,** Patent. **15,** Concise. **18,** Pea. **19,** Inn. **21,** Dray. **23,** Motor. **24,** Crib. **27,** Net. **29,** Day. **31,** Riddled. **32,** Peered. **34,** Also. **35,** Eleven. **38,** Laden. **39,** Groyne. **40,** Atlas. **Down: 2,** Eke. **3,** Prince. **4,** Ten. **5,** Slip. **6,** Rooted. **7,** Neatly. **9,** Version. **12,** Rap **13,** Near. **16,** Over. **17,** Enter. **20,** Noticed. **22,** Able. **24,** Coping. **25,** Idea. **26,** Barley. **28,** Advent. **30,** Yes. **33,** Dole. **36,** Lea. **37,** Era.

PUZZLE No. 216. Across 2, Burst. 7, True. 8, Origin. 9, Tempt. 11, Can. 13, Rid. 15, Edam. 16, Rim. 18, Beau. 19, Piloted. 20, Tore. 22, Dull. 23, Against. 25, Alto. 27, Due. 28, Fear. 30, Lie. 31, Did. 33, Sense. 36, Chance. 37, Knew. 38, Terse. **Down:** 1, Broad. 2, Bet. 3, Ram. 4, Tot. 5, Dig. 6, Tibia. 10, Pail. 11, Central. 12, Narrate. 13, Reduced. 14, Dullard. 16, Rigid. 17, Morse. 18, Bed. 21, Ego. 24, Nude. 26, Lithe. 29, Aided. 32, End. 33, Set. 34, Nor. 35, Eke.

PUZZLE No. 217. Across 2, Adore. 7, Stare. 8, Legal. 10, Offer. 12, Cot. 13, Close. 15, Decided. 17, Reveal. 19, Cut. 20, Tutored. 23, More. 25, Dear. 26, Tangled. 30, Sea. 31, Repute. 34, Besiege. 37, Cited. 38, Rue. 39, Extol. 40, Geese. 41, Debit. 42, Steed. **Down** 1, Stole. 2, Arose. 3, Defeat. 4, Reed. 5, Recited. 6, Hated. 9, God. 11, Recover. 13, Crime. 14, Overt. 16, Cur. 18, Luggage. 21, Debut. 22, Greed. 24, Easiest. 27, Nee. 28, Decode. 29, Beret. 32, Piled. 33, Tepid. 35, Sue. 36, Exit.

PUZZLE No. 218. Across: 1, Send. 4, War. 6, Wept. 8, Prison. 9, Method. 10, Tap. 12, Flood. 14, Groom. 15, Beset. 18, Talent. 20, Issued 24, Yacht. 26, Shaft. 28, Yield. 30, Ale. 32, Redeem. 33, Detail. 34, Bend. 35, Doe. 36, Nigh. **Down:** 2, Enrol. 3, Disrobe. 4, Want. 5, Ramp. 6, Water. 7, Provoke. 11, Awe. 12, Fat. 13, Den. 16, Sty. 17, Tic. 19, Achieve. 21, Shy. 22, Stilton. 23, Dad. 25, Ail. 27, Freed. 29, Lying. 30, Amid. 31, Edge.

PUZZLE No. 219. Across 1, Vanish. 5, Secure. 8, Belittle. 9, Rude. 10, Cat. 12, Slope. 15, Sot. 17, Art. 18, Jet. 19, Oil. 20, Alive. 21, Ore. 22, Oar. 23, Car. 24, Ken. 26, Tight. 29, Eat. 33, Sure. 34, Scuttled. 35, Pledge. 36, Enmity. **Down:** 2, Arena. 3, Iris. 4, Hotel. 5, Sleep. 6, Core. 7, Radio. 10, Clock. 11, Talon. 12, Start. 13, Owing. 14, Eject. 15, Store. 16, Treat. 25, Equal. 27, Issue. 28, House. 30, Avert. 31, Lead. 32, Stem.

PUZZLE No. 220. Across 1, Aged. 4, Cow. 6, Also. 9, Dip. 10, Convince. 11, Item. 14, Aid. 16, Lucky. 19, Retained. 21, Repel. 23, Donation. 24, Panic. 27, Top. 31, Muse. 33, Manacled. 34, Tea. 35, Feel. 36, Tie. 37, Name. **Down:** 2, Grow. 3, Dive. 4, Confined. 5, Weep. 6, Adieu. 7, Lit. 8, Speak. 12, Creep. 13, Stain. 14, Air. 15, Depot. 17, Civil. 18, Young. 20, Denounce. 22, Lap. 25, Acute. 26, Ideal. 28, Smut. 29, Scan. 30, Team. 32, See.

PUZZLE No. 221. Across 4, Pagan. 7, Ticket. 9, Hem. 10, Wed. 12, Reach. 13, Plea. 15, Resin. 17, Prompt. 19, Dirt. 20, Eaten. 22, Ram. 24, Alleged. 27, Yes. 28, Naked. 31, Less. 33, Assure. 35, Panel. 37, Tear. 38, Relax. 39, Dam. 41, Red. 42, Pallid. 43, Steed. **Down:** 1, Staple. 2, Accept. 3, New. 4, Peri. 5, Amend. 6, Accurate. 8, Term. 11, Depressed. 14, Area. 16, Stag. 18, Only. 21, Adherent. 23, Menu. 25, Lean. 26, Dart. 29, Keenly. 30, Deride. 32, Spare. 34, Slap. 36, Axed. 40, Mat.

PUZZLE No. 222. Across 1, Divert. 5, Deduct. 9, Oiled. 10, Fiesta. 11, Person. 12, Arson. 14, Lees. 17, Act. 18, Sole. 20, Ended. 22, Motor. 23, Wastrel. 24, Renew. 26, Timid. 29, Arid. 30, Jet. 32, Dice. 33, Harem. 35, Hugged. 36, Nausea. 37, Refer. 38, Reeled. 39, Tended. **Down:** 1, Defile. 2, Veered. 3, Rota. 4, Tiara. 5, Depot. 6, Eden. 7, Upshot. 8, Tinker. 13, Scatter. 15, Enter. 16, Sewed. 18, Solid. 19, Logic. 21, Daw. 22, Met. 24, Rather. 25, Niggle. 27, Missed. 28, Demand. 30, Jaded. 31, Tenet. 33, Here. 34, Mare.

PUZZLE No. 223. Across 3, Water. 9, Roster. 10, Volume. 11, Breed. 12, Acid. 15, Rage. 17, Torrent. 20, Lot. 21, Tempt. 23, Frog. 25, Tour. 26, Panic. 28, Ass. 30, Donated. 33, Used. 35, Late. 36, Rumba. 38, Useful. 39, Ascent. 40, Berth. **Down:** 1, Treat. 2, Astir. 3, Web. 4, Arrant. 4, Ever. 6, Rod. 7, Rural. 8, Beret. 13, Confess. 14, Droop. 16, Gourmet. 18, Tepid. 19, Apt. 22, Total. 24, Gap. 27, Combat. 28, Augur. 29, Sewer. 31, Tamed. 32, Death. 34, Rule. 36, Rub. 37, Ash.

PUZZLE No. 224. Across 1, Reduce. **5,** Damp. **8,** Tonic. **9,** Cos. **10,** Deer. **11,** Ship. **12,** Agree. **13,** Teller. **16,** Left. **18,** Scan. **20,** Asp. **22,** Pet. **23,** Eel. **24,** Tier. **25,** Ewer. **28,** Nursed. **30,** Elite. **32,** Aura. **33,** Anon. **34,** Rue. **35,** Stand. **36,** Knee. **37,** Bridge. **Down: 1,** Recite. **2,** Disclose. **3,** Cudgel. **4,** Forgotten. **5,** Disease. **6,** Ache. **7,** Pipe. **8,** Tea. **14,** Repentant. **15,** Pal. **17,** Few. **19,** Censured. **20,** Ail. **21,** Prelate. **26,** Runner. **27,** Adhere. **29,** Tank. **30,** Erse. **31,** End.

NOTES